THEORY OF ELECTRONS

THEORY OF ELECTRONS

BY

L. ROSENFELD

PROFESSOR OF THEORETICAL PHYSICS
IN THE UNIVERSITY OF MANCHESTER

DOVER PUBLICATIONS, INC., NEW YORK

Published in Canada by General Publishing Company, Ltd., 30 Lesmill Road, Don Mills, Toronto, Ontario.
Published in the United Kingdom by Constable and Company, Ltd., 10 Orange Street, London W. C. 2.

This Dover edition, first published in 1965, is an unabridged and corrected republication of the work first published by North-Holland Publishing Company, Amsterdam, in 1951. This edition, which contains a new Preface by the author, is published by special arrangement with North-Holland Publishing Company.

Library of Congress Catalog Card Number 65-26028

Manufactured in the United States of America

Dover Publications, Inc.
180 Varick Street
New York, N. Y. 10014

*To my Dutch colleagues and students
in grateful memory of the years spent
in their midst*

H. A. Lorentz

PREFACE TO THE DOVER EDITION

The present edition of this little book is identical to the first, except that a few misprints and minor errors have been corrected. Actually, I would have preferred to revise the text in the light of recent investigations, some of which are directly related to its contents. The main reason which has so far delayed this revision is that it should include, as I shall presently explain, an extension of the rigorous theory of dispersion, and this I have not yet found how to present in harmony with the elementary character of the book. All I can do for the moment is to call the reader's attention to a few points of particular interest which have emerged from recent work.

An important question of general method has been raised by P. Mazur[1]. Instead of the consideration of space-time averages of atomic quantities over physically infinitesimal elements, Mazur advocates a systematic use of averages defined according to the principles of statistical mechanics. It is undeniable that this method —which Lorentz himself, and also Niels Bohr, applied with supreme mastery to the classical electron theory of metals—presents advantages of formal elegance and great generality, but it does not give as detailed a physical picture of the underlying atomic processes as the other. Moreover, a formalism which makes use of the concepts of charge and current densities at the atomic level is immediately adapted to a quantal description of the atomic systems, whereas the formalism of statistical mechanics has an essentially different structure according as whether the atomic systems are treated classically or quantally. These two circumstances seem to me of such weight, from the didactic point of view, that within the limited scope of this book I should not propose even in a thoroughly revised edition to abandon the mode of exposition I have chosen in the second chapter. If anything, I would rather extend it to the other

[1] Mazur has given an excellent exposition of his method, with full references to the relevant papers, in *Advances in Chemical Physics*, vol. I (New York, 1958), pp. 309–60.

chapters also, were it not that to do this in the spirit of the correspondence principle would require more elaborate classical dynamics than I want to presuppose.

In another respect, however, I should like to improve, in the second chapter, the discussion of the averages of the electromagnetic quantities, so as to make clearer their relationship to the basic definitions of the macroscopic field quantities given by W. Thomson and Maxwell. I would thus remove an imperfection of the present treatment, which has been pointed out by A. N. Kaufman[2]. The electric quadrupole tensor q ought to be defined as traceless, so as to vanish for a charge distribution of spherical symmetry; i.e. the definition (15) of Chapter II ought to be modified by adding a term $q(P)\mathsf{U}$, where U is the unit tensor and

$$q(P) = -\tfrac{1}{6} \int_{\text{atom}} dv_a\, \varrho(P, \mathbf{r}) r_a^2.$$

It is readily seen that the contribution of the quadrupole moment to the electric displacement keeps the same form after this modification, but that the average field intensity $\bar{\mathbf{e}}$ must *not* be identified with the macroscopic field intensity $\mathbf{E}$; the correct relationship is

$$\bar{\mathbf{e}} = \mathbf{E} - \operatorname{grad} Q,$$

where Q is defined in terms of q by a formula of the type (19), (20), viz.

$$Q(P) = \sum_{\theta} q(P) N_{\theta}(P).$$

This correction is clearly of little practical significance, but it is interesting in showing that the higher multipole moments also affect, in regions of inhomogeneity, the averages of the field quantities, and not just those of the charge and current densities.

In developing the theory of optical dispersion, I have everywhere allowed the refractive index to have an arbitrary value, in order to exhibit its influence on the various phenomena studied. On the other hand, I have been anxious to demonstrate the general structure and consistency of the theory as simply as the inherent complexity of the

[2] A. N. Kaufman, *American Journ. of Physics*, **29**, 626, 1961.

subject would allow, and for this didactic reason I have only taken the correlations between the scattering systems into account to the lowest order. In the approach I have adopted, this entails, in particular, a difference in the treatment of the transmitted and the scattered wave which is sometimes not realistic (near the critical point, for instance), and the analysis of the effect of the correlations ought to be carried at least one step further; but such an analysis, according to investigations currently pursued by Dr. Bullough, at once introduces great complications, to which no short cut has yet been found.

It should be mentioned, in this connexion, that instead of the approximation I started from, and in which the scattered wave is described as a wave propagated *in vacuo*, one could base the treatment on the other extreme assumption—that it is propagated in the medium like the transmitted wave: this procedure, adopted by Fixman[3], has been developed in a very elegant way by Mazur and Postma[4]. Although such an approximation incorporates from the start a contribution from the higher correlations to the scattered wave, it is not obvious that it describes the main effect of these correlations; in any case, it does not absolve us from the task of working out the following steps, which are just as laborious as in the other alternative[5]. The derivation of a precise expression for the scattering coefficients of media in which the scattering systems are strongly correlated is not a merely academic problem, but has also considerable practical interest: methods of determination of molecular weights and shapes of polymers, for instance, are based on the study of their scattering power in solution[6].

Manchester, 1965

[3] M. Fixman, *J. Chem. Phys.*, 23, 2074, 1955.
[4] P. Mazur, *loc. cit.*, pp. 350–56.
[5] This point is discussed by R. K. Bullough, *Phil. Trans. A*, **258**, 38f, 1965.
[6] See the paper just quoted by R. K. Bullough, as well as his previous one in *Proc. Roy. Soc. A*, **275**, 271, 1963.

PREFACE TO THE FIRST EDITION

The present book is a revised and somewhat extended version of a course of lectures which I have given from time to time to advanced students in the Universities of Liège, Utrecht and Manchester. Its purpose is not to give any comprehensive account of the electric, magnetic and optical properties of matter, but rather to provide a framework for such an account, by discussing the establishment of the foundations on which the atomistic interpretation of these properties rests. It seems to me that such an outline of the main ideas of a physical theory, sufficiently precise to serve as a starting-point for further studies, may have its place beside more elaborate treatises in which the emphasis is laid on the detailed analysis of experimental data. It goes without saying that the distinction between the two types of treatment can never be very sharp: it is just as impossible to survey a subject without going into the underlying principles as to examine these principles without reference to specific applications. Thus, while I might describe my endeavour as an attempt to reduce the theory to a skeleton, I have nevertheless been careful to spare some meaty morsels.

The subject, by its very nature, does not admit of elementary treatment. The reader is assumed to have some familiarity with the fundamental ideas of the statistical description of matter, the methods of analytical mechanics, and Maxwell's theory of the electromagnetic field. On the other hand, the discussion is kept on a classical basis throughout, in the sense that no explicit use is made of the techniques of quantum theory; however, care has been taken to indicate the kind of modifications rendered necessary by quantal effects, especially in those cases, such as magnetism and optical dispersion, in which quantum theory plays an essential role. A large part of the classical theory of electrons, however, is of such a generality as to remain formally valid when a quantal description of atomic systems is introduced. A notable exception is the theory of metals: the behaviour of electrons in metals is dominated to such an extent by the exclusion principle that it would be futile to attempt any comprehensive discussion of metallic properties along classical lines. Apart from a few instances in which this could still be done without difficulty, I have therefore left metals out of consideration altogether, referring the reader to special treatises.

In the preparation of the text, I have been greatly helped in every possible way by Dr J. Podolanski and Mr J. Maddox. Both kindly went through the manuscript with great care, and I owe many improvements to their stimulating criticism. Nobody, however, could tell me how to reconcile the adoption of rational electromagnetic units with the practical necessity of referring to experimental results expressed in the older system of units, so I gave it up in despair.

I am grateful to Prof. W. J. de Haas for the permission to reproduce a striking portrait of Lorentz and for an interesting correspondence concerning the early history of the discovery of the electron. I also wish to thank Prof. J. de Boer for his most obliging help and valuable advice in deciding on the system of notation outlined in the Appendix. In the selection of the appropriate letter types, as well as in all other typographical problems which arose, the publisher spared no effort to meet my wishes. The production of a book like this within four months of the delivery of the manuscript is certainly a highly praise-worthy achievement.

In keeping with the aim of the book, the historical introduction has been deliberately reduced to a somewhat schematized outline; I am keenly conscious, of course, of the danger inherent in such a procedure, and have done my best to avoid distortion of the historical perspective. On the other hand, one may think that the share taken by optical problems is such as to upset the balance of the book. I might adduce some solemn argument for my defence, as for instance the lack of any easily accessible treatment of similar scope. I prefer to confess, however, that my chief reason for dwelling on these problems has been sheer delight in the harmony they reveal between our finest perceptions of phenomena so beautiful and the mental representation we have been able to form of them.

Manchester, October 1950

CONTENTS

V. ELECTRIC POLARIZATION AND OPTICAL DISPERSION

VI. RIGOROUS THEORY OF DISPERSION

Note. Formulae are numbered separately in each chapter. Formula (33) of Chapter V, say, is referred to as (33) in Chapter V, and as (V, 33) in any other chapter.

LIST OF SYMBOLS

$U(P,P')$ Green's function for retarded potentials 101

V volume

$\mathbf{v}$ velocity

W Weiss factor of internal field 52

$\mathbf{x}_k$ space coordinate of kth particle 28

a degree of orientation of dipoles 48, 53, 61, extinction or scattering coefficient for perfect gases 69, 74

a' extinction or scattering coefficient (general) 85, 109

a_e scattering coefficient for free electrons 80

$a(\theta)$ differential scattering coefficient 77, 85

β coefficient of absorption per wave-length 69, coefficient of isothermal compressibility 81

γ total electric polarizability per unit volume 62, 90 Euler's constant

γ_a molecular electric polarizability 60

γ_d electric polarizability due to permanent dipoles 61

γ_e induced electric polarizability per unit volume 60

γ_{mol} electric polarizability per gram-molecule 65

Γ_k line width 69

δ mass density 65

ε range of direct correlation function 83, 85, dielectric constant 63

$\eta = -e/2mc$ factor of Larmor frequency 34

θ angle of scattering 75, Eulerian angle 48

Θ Curie point 53, 54

$\varkappa$ dielectric susceptibility 63, range of correlation function 84

μ molecular weight 65

μ_0 Bohr magneton 51

μ_J component of atomic magnetic moment in direction of angular momentum 38

μ magnetic dipole moment of atom 25, 44

μ_d induced magnetic dipole moment 45

μ_s spin magnetic moment of electron 37

μ_S spin magnetic moment of atom 38

ϱ charge density 13

ϱ_f spatial density of free charge 20

ϱ_t density of true charge 17

σ circular wave number 85

σ_f superficial density of free charge 19, 20

σ spin angular momentum 37

τ light path 13

φ scalar potential 29, Eulerian angle 48

$\varphi_j, \varphi_\zeta, \Phi$ phase factors 76, 77, 78

χ_d diamagnetic susceptibility 45

χ_p paramagnetic susceptibility 50

ψ Eulerian angle 48

ω circular frequency

ω_k proper frequency of atomic oscillator 65

ω_L Larmor frequency 10, 35

ω angular velocity 35

ω_L Larmor precession velocity 10, 34

THEORY OF ELECTRONS

CHAPTER I

INTRODUCTION

Maxwell's theory is a *phenomenological* theory, in the sense that it describes the electric and magnetic properties of matter by means of certain parameters, such as the density of electric or magnetic polarization, without seeking to make any further analysis of the origin of these quantities. To provide an analysis of this kind is precisely the task of the *theory of electrons*, in which the electromagnetic properties of matter are considered from the point of view of *atomic theory*.

We here proceed a step further than in statistical mechanics, where only the *existence* of atoms as mechanical systems is assumed. Now we must go deeper into the *structure* of the atoms, and especially into the nature of their electrically charged constituent particles. We shall start with a brief historical review * of the most fundamental discoveries which gradually led to a complete picture of the electrical constitution of atoms.

1. CONDUCTION OF ELECTRICITY IN ELECTROLYTES

It may seem strange that the first insight into the *atomic nature of electricity* did not come from the study of the best conductors, the metals. As we now know, conduction of electricity in metals is not associated with a transport of matter; there was therefore no obvious necessity to picture it as a flow of electrified particles.

The first hint of the existence of "quanta" of electricity was derived from the investigation of the convective mechanism of

---

* The classical history of the subject is E.T. Whittaker's *History of the Theories of Aether and Electricity* (Dublin, 1910). It gives a masterly account of the evolution of our ideas about electricity, magnetism and optics from the first beginnings.

electrical conduction operative in electrolytes. Faraday's masterly
analysis (1833) led to the well-known law that *each gram-atom of
a univalent electrolyte transports the same quantity of electricity.*
This charge, approximately 96500 coulombs, is now called a
faraday. From the law just enunciated, the immediate conclusion
is drawn that if the gram-atom of electrolyte consists of a certain
number of identical atoms, each of these transports the same
definite quantity of electricity, which constitutes, so to speak,
an "atom of electric charge". Faraday himself was very cautious
about this inference, because he was unwilling to consider the
atomic theory of matter as something more than a convenient
hypothesis, or terminology. In fact, it was only in 1881, when the
fruitfulness of atomic theory had been successfully put to the test
by the intervening expansion of chemistry, that the existence of
an *elementary electric charge* was reasserted and the name *electron*
given to it.

According to Faraday's terminology, the atoms or radicals carrying
the electric current in electrolytes are called *ions.* The electron,
therefore, is the charge carried by a univalent ion. The value e
of this charge is given by

$$Le = F,$$

where F denotes the faraday and L Avogadro's number, which is
the number of atoms in one gram-atom.

2. CONDUCTION OF ELECTRICITY IN GASES

At the time when the existence of the electron was recognized in
this way, the properties of electrical discharges through gases at
reduced pressures were being actively investigated. This line of
investigation had also been initiated by Faraday (1838), but
progress, closely dependent on the development of vacuum-pump
technique, had been slow. The discovery (1869) of *cathode rays,*
however, and the study of their properties which showed them to
be corpuscular carriers of negative electricity, eventually led
Schuster (1884) to suggest that the conduction of electricity in
rarefied gases, like that of electrolytes, is due to a splitting of the

molecules into ions. In the course of the investigation of cathode rays it was discovered by Röntgen (1895) that these rays, on hitting the glass of the discharge tube or a metallic anticathode specially placed in the tube, produce a penetrating radiation, which he called *X-rays*. The X-rays were interpreted by Schuster as an electromagnetic radiation of very high frequency, emitted, in accordance with Maxwell's theory, by the charged cathodic corpuscles owing to their deceleration at the anticathode. The importance of X-rays for the study of electric conduction through gases lies in their great *ionizing power*. A gas irradiated by an X-ray tube acquires, even at ordinary pressures, a considerable conductivity, which is thus amenable to a detailed quantitative analysis.

Thanks to this improved technique, J. J. Thomson and his pupils at the Cavendish Laboratory were able to prove quite generally the ionic character of gaseous conduction and to establish its quantitative laws. In particular, they found that if a gas between the plates of a condenser is made conducting, the current, so long as the ionization is sufficiently weak, is proportional to the potential difference V between the plates. In terms of the ionic picture of the conduction process this law may be interpreted by observing that in moving through the gas an ion undergoes a resistance proportional to its velocity. In the steady state of motion the constant velocity v acquired by an ion of charge e under the combined action of the accelerating force due to the electric field E and of the frictional resistance $-v/B$ is given by

$$eE - \frac{v}{B} = 0, \quad \text{or} \quad v = eBE.$$

If there are, on the average, N ions of charge e per unit volume, their contribution to the current, as long as effects of space charge may be neglected, will thus be

$$Nev = Ne^2BE,$$

and since E is proportional to V, the same is true for the total current.

The preceding argument shows that the velocity of the ions in an electric field is proportional to this field. We may write

$$v = v_0 E, \quad \text{with} \quad v_0 = eB.$$

The parameter v_0, the velocity of an ion in a unit electric field, is called the *mobility* of the ion. It is related to the *coefficient of diffusion D* of the ions in the gas by the relation

$$D = BkT,$$

well known from the kinetic theory of gases; in this formula T is the absolute temperature of the gas and k is Boltzmann's constant. Instead of the temperature we may introduce the pressure p of the gas, which is given in the kinetic theory by

$$p = nkT,$$

n being the average number of gas molecules per unit volume. Combining the last three formulae, we get

$$ne = \frac{v_0}{D} \cdot p.$$

Measurements of the mobility and diffusion coefficient of ions of a given kind will therefore give an estimate of the product ne. It was thus ascertained for the first time that the charges of gaseous ions are of the same order of magnitude as those of the ions present in electrolytes; i.e. we again meet here with the elementary electronic charge.

Moreover, the values obtained for the diffusion coefficients of both positive and negative ions at ordinary pressures are much smaller than those of gas molecules. This shows that at such pressures the ions consist of "clusters" of molecules held together by electrostatic forces. On the other hand, the cathode-ray particles, which play a prominent part in the conduction at very low pressures, exhibit a quite different behaviour. In 1894 Lenard succeeded in obtaining cathode rays outside the discharge tube by letting them pass through a thin aluminium "window". He found that the cathodic corpuscles have such a great penetrating power that they must be much smaller than ordinary atoms. This conclusion, though puzzling, seemed to point to some fundamental feature of the cathodic corpuscles as carriers of negative electricity. The real clue to an understanding of their nature, however, was first obtained when it proved possible to determine the ratio of charge to mass of the *individual* corpuscles.

3. THOMSON'S DETERMINATION OF THE SPECIFIC CHARGE

Charged particles moving with a given velocity in a constant electric or magnetic field perpendicular to the velocity are deflected from their course in different directions: the electric deflection is parallel to the electric field, the magnetic deflection is perpendicular to both magnetic field and velocity. The two deflections depend on the nature of the particle in exactly the same way: they are both proportional to the ratio of the charge to the mass of the particle, which we shall call its *specific charge*. Their dependence on the velocity v of the particle, however, is different: after a small length of path l under the action of the respective fields the electric deflection will be proportional to $(l/v)^2$ (since the motion in the electric field is uniformly accelerated during the time l/v), while the magnetic deflection will be proportional to l^2/v (since in this case the path is a small arc of length l of a circle whose radius is proportional to v).

Let e, m denote the charge and mass of the particle; E, H the electric and magnetic field strengths; and D_e, D_m the electric and magnetic deflections for a small length of path l. We have, in the first place, for a constant acceleration eE/m during the time l/v,

$$D_e = \frac{1}{2} \cdot \frac{eE}{m} \cdot \left(\frac{l}{v}\right)^2.$$

The acceleration due to the magnetic field is given by the law of the action of such a field on an element of current ev; its magnitude is evH/mc (c being the velocity of light), and it is at each instant perpendicular to the velocity. The latter therefore remains constant in magnitude, and the trajectory is a circle, whose radius R is

obtained by equating the centripetal acceleration due to the magnetic field to the centrifugal acceleration v^2/R. This gives

$$\frac{1}{R} = \frac{|e|H}{mc} \cdot \frac{1}{v}.$$

Therefore,

$$D_m = R\{1 - \cos(l/R)\} \approx \tfrac{1}{2} R\left(\frac{l}{R}\right)^2 = \frac{1}{2} \cdot \frac{|e|H}{mc} \cdot \frac{l^2}{v}.$$

Measurements of both electric and magnetic deflection of an ion
will thus in principle lead to a determination of its velocity and
its specific charge. The idea of this method is due to J. J. Thomson,
who first applied it (1897) to an estimation of the specific charge
of cathode rays. The surprising result was that the specific charge
of a cathodic corpuscle is about 2000 times *larger* than that of the
lightest univalent ion, the hydrogen ion, in electrolytes. It seemed
reasonable to assume (and it was soon proved, as we shall see, by
direct measurements) that the charge carried by the corpuscles
is the electronic charge; it must then be concluded that the masses
of the corpuscles are about 2000 times *smaller* than that of the
lightest atom. This conclusion gained in strength when it was
verified that the cathodic corpuscles are all identical, irrespective
of the nature of the gas in which the discharge is produced. They
appear, therefore, as "atoms of electricity", with a much smaller
mass than any material atom, and since they can be split off from
such atoms, they must play a fundamental part in their constitution. In extension of its original meaning, the word *electron* is
now used to denote such corpuscles of small mass carrying an
elementary charge. Although there are, as we now know, electrons
of both signs, we shall only be concerned, in the following, with
those of negative charge, which alone appear as stable constituents
of ordinary matter.
The positive ions taking part in the discharge can be isolated in
the form of *canal rays* by using a perforated cathode: the positive
ions pass through the holes, or canals, of the cathode and into
that part of the tube behind the cathode, where they can be conveniently studied. Deflection measurements revealed that the

specific charges of these positive ions are of the order of magnitude to be expected for ordinary atoms or molecules of the gas investigated carrying one or in some cases two or three elementary charges. The ionization of the molecules can therefore be pictured as the splitting off of one or a few electrons from the neutral molecule, leaving a positively charged fragment which retains practically the whole mass of the molecule. This at once leads to the view that the constituent part of an atom or molecule which is associated with the bulk of its mass is also positively charged, while an equivalent negative charge is present in the form of a certain number of electrons of very small mass.

For the purpose of deriving in a general way the electromagnetic properties of matter in bulk from the electric constitution of atoms, the atomic model just outlined is sufficient; there will be no need to specify more accurately the spatial distribution of the positive electricity in the atom. The situation would be different, of course, if we wanted to perform actual calculations of electric or magnetic parameters; but then, we should have to use the methods of quantum mechanics, which we want to keep outside the scope of our present considerations. We shall not, therefore, follow any further the development of the study of atomic constitution; let us just recall that the discovery of radioactivity by the Curies, made at about the same time as Thomson's discovery of the electron, eventually led Rutherford (1911) to the establishment of the *nuclear model* of the atom, according to which the positive electricity and practically the whole mass of the atom are concentrated in a *nucleus* of linear dimensions 10^4 to 10^5 times smaller than those of the atom. An improved form of Thomson's deflection method for the measurement of the specific charges of positive ions showed that there are nuclei of the same chemical element (i.e. the same nuclear charge) with different masses, the so-called *isotopes*. The method has nowadays been elaborated to high-precision *mass spectrography*.

If the electric and magnetic fields are applied simultaneously in the same direction, the deflections D_e, D_m will be at right angles, and the traces of the deflected ions on a photographic plate perpendicular to the (undeflected) path will be distributed along *parabolas* defined by the equation

$$D_e = \frac{2\,mc^2\,E}{eH^2\,l^2}\,D_m^2,$$

each parabola corresponding to a definite value of the specific charge. This powerful method thus permits a complete analysis of inhomogeneous beams of positive ions.

4. DETERMINATION OF THE ELEMENTARY CHARGE

The first attempt to estimate the average charge carried by a gaseous ion was made by Townsend (1897). He used the fact that such ions act as nuclei of condensation for supersaturated water vapour. He observed the velocity of fall of the condensation cloud, measured its total weight and collected its total charge. The velocity of fall, using Stokes' law, yields the average mass of a cloud droplet; from the total weight, the number of droplets is thus estimated, and the average charge carried by an ion then follows from the total charge measured. The charge value estimated in this rather crude way is of the order of magnitude expected for an electron. The agreement was at any rate sufficient to corroborate the conclusions drawn from the specific charge measurements concerning the nature of the cathodic corpuscles.

The decisive step in the problem, however, was made by Millikan (1910) when he succeeded in isolating a single charged oil droplet and observing its motion under the combined action of gravity and a vertical electric field. This method permits a precision determination of the electronic charge. For ordinary purposes it is sufficient to remember the approximate figure

$$|e| = 4.80 \cdot 10^{-10} \text{ c.g.s. electrostatic units.}$$

Combined with the specific charge

$$\frac{|e|}{m} = 5.27 \cdot 10^{17} \text{ c.g.s. electrostatic units,}$$

this gives for the electronic mass

$$m = 0.91 \cdot 10^{-27} \text{ g},$$

i.e. approximately 1/1840 of the mass of the hydrogen nucleus. If, on the other hand, we combine the absolute determination of the elementary charge with the value of the faraday, we obtain the accurate value

$$L = 6.02 \cdot 10^{23}$$

for Avogadro's number, the number of atoms in a gram-atom.

5. THE ZEEMAN EFFECT

Powerful support for Thomson's view of atomic constitution was afforded by Zeeman's slightly earlier discovery of the influence of a magnetic field on the frequency of light emitted by atoms and the theoretical analysis of this effect by Lorentz. In order to understand the Zeeman effect we must first have a picture of the emission of light by undisturbed atoms. Lorentz assumed that this emission is due to harmonic oscillations of charged corpuscles (eventually identified with electrons) within the atom. If ω_0 denotes the circular frequency of such an oscillator and $\mathbf{x}$ its amplitude, the equations of motion are

$$\ddot{\mathbf{x}} + \omega_0^2 \, \mathbf{x} = 0$$

and the emitted electromagnetic radiation has the same circular frequency ω_0. In other words, to each line of the spectrum of the atom a harmonic oscillator with the same proper frequency is associated. This is, of course, a very crude picture; but a comparison with the modern treatment of the problem of light emission by atoms by the methods of quantum mechanics shows that this simple model nevertheless exhibits the essential qualitative features of the phenomena. It is even possible to establish a *correspondence* between the radiative properties of the actual atomic systems and those of "virtual" oscillators of the kind we are considering. We shall therefore, here and in the following, keep to Lorentz' oscillator model.

A constant magnetic field **H** exerts on our oscillator, considered as an element of current $e\dot{\mathbf{x}}$, a force

$$\mathbf{F} = \frac{e}{c}\, \dot{\mathbf{x}} \wedge \mathbf{H},$$

the so-called *Lorentz force*; if the mass of the oscillating particle is m, the corresponding acceleration is $\mathbf{F}/m$, and the equations of motion become

$$\ddot{\mathbf{x}} + 2\dot{\mathbf{x}} \wedge \omega_L + \omega_0^2\, \mathbf{x} = 0,$$

with the notation

$$\omega_L = -\frac{e}{2mc}\, \mathbf{H}.$$

The vector ω_L involves only the specific charge of the oscillator. According to the sign of e, it is parallel or antiparallel to the magnetic field. In the following analysis we shall use the algebraic quantity

$$\omega_L = -\frac{e}{2mc}\, H,$$

where H denotes the absolute value of the vector **H**.

The component of the oscillation in a direction parallel to the magnetic field is, of course, unaffected. To describe the motion in the plane (x, y) perpendicular to the magnetic field it is convenient to introduce the complex variable $\xi = x + iy$. The undisturbed equations of motion in the plane take the form

$$\ddot{\xi} + \omega_0^2\, \xi = 0$$

and the solutions $\xi \sim \exp(\pm i\,\omega_0 t)$ correspond to circular motions of the oscillator and consequently to the emission of circularly polarized radiation in directions perpendicular to the plane; the plus sign in the exponent corresponds to left-handed polarization of the light emitted in the positive normal direction. In the presence of the magnetic field the equations of motion in the plane become

$$\ddot{\xi} - 2i\omega_L\dot{\xi} + \omega_0^2\, \xi = 0$$

and still have solutions of the form $\xi \sim \exp(\pm i\omega t)$ with circular frequencies ω given by

$$\omega^2 \mp 2\,\omega_L\,\omega - \omega_0^2 = 0,$$

i.e.

$$\omega = \sqrt{(\omega_0^2 + \omega_L^2)} \pm \omega_L,$$

or approximately, if $\omega_L \ll \omega_0$,

$$\omega \approx \omega_0 \pm \omega_L.$$

The frequencies of the circularly polarized components are therefore symmetrically displaced with respect to the original frequency by the amount $|\omega_L|$. Observation in the direction of the magnetic field will thus show a *doublet* of displaced lines with opposite circular polarizations. If the charge e is negative, and therefore $\omega_L > 0$, the polarization of the line of greater frequency will be left-handed. In directions normal to the magnetic field one will observe a *triplet* of linearly polarized radiations, consisting of the undisplaced component parallel to the magnetic field and the symmetrically displaced ones perpendicular to the field.

These theoretical predictions refer to the so-called *normal* Zeeman effect, which is only observed for a special class of spectral lines. In most cases complications occur which give rise to *anomalous* Zeeman patterns; we shall not enter into this question here. The measurement of the frequency change ω_L in a given magnetic field yields the specific charge of the oscillator responsible for the emission of the spectral line considered. Zeeman's determinations immediately led Lorentz to infer that the masses of these oscillators must be much smaller than those of material ions. In fact, when a year later * Thomson's estimate of the specific charge of the cathodic corpuscles became available, no doubt

---

* As Prof. W. J. de Haas kindly pointed out to me, the sequence of events leading to the discovery of the electron is frequently misrepresented. Zeeman's discovery, together with the clear recognition by Lorentz of its implications, dates from October 1896, while Thomson's cathode ray experiments were performed in 1897.

was left as to the identity of Lorentz' oscillators with electrons, in harmony with Thomson's atomic model.

It will be observed that in the preceding theory of the Zeeman effect the motion of the positive constituents of the atom has been entirely neglected. Such a neglect is justified by the great difference in mass between those positive constituents and the electrons. This explains why almost the whole theory of the electromagnetic properties of matter can be developed without precise knowledge of the distribution of the positive electricity within the atom, and thus deserves the traditional name of "theory of electrons".

CHAPTER II

ATOMISTIC FOUNDATION OF MAXWELL'S THEORY

We shall now present the foundations of the theory of electrons essentially as they have been laid by H. A. Lorentz (1895) *. The mode of presentation will, of course, be adapted to modern ideas on the constitution of matter, and the theory carried to a somewhat greater degree of generality. In particular, the distribution of charge and current in the atoms will be left unspecified; the theory thus remains formally valid when the atomic systems are treated according to the principles of quantum theory.

1. FORMULATION OF THE PROBLEM

From the point of view of the electromagnetic theory an atom or ion is characterized by a distribution of electric charge and current of respective densities ϱ, $\mathbf{i}$. These distributions are confined to the region of space occupied by the atomic system, and they will generally vary in time in a more or less irregular way. If the currents are due to the motion of the charges with a velocity $\mathbf{v}$ defined at each point of space and each instant, we may write, in electromagnetic units, $\mathbf{i} = \varrho \mathbf{v}/c$.

The electromagnetic field $\mathbf{e}$, $\mathbf{h}$ due to such charge and current distributions satisfies at any point of space and any instant the equations of Maxwell in the simple form they take *in vacuo*, viz.

$$\operatorname{curl} \mathbf{h} = \mathbf{i} + \frac{\partial \mathbf{e}}{\partial \tau}, \quad \operatorname{curl} \mathbf{e} = -\frac{\partial \mathbf{h}}{\partial \tau}$$
$$\operatorname{div} \mathbf{e} = \varrho \quad , \quad \operatorname{div} \mathbf{h} = 0. \tag{1}$$

In these formulae Heaviside units are used, and the time τ is measured in light-seconds (i.e. $\tau = ct$). This "microscopic" field will exhibit large and irregular variations both in space and in

---

* Lorentz' famous book, *The Theory of Electrons* (Leipzig, 1909), still repays careful study.

time. It is not the field, however, which is dealt with in usual electrodynamics. Field quantities on the macroscopic scale are averages of the corresponding microscopic quantities taken over spatial regions and time intervals which are large compared with atomic dimensions and periods. Such space-time regions, although containing many atoms and extending in time over many atomic periods, may still be sufficiently small with respect to the macroscopic scale to be regarded as infinitesimal: they are sometimes called "physically infinitesimal". The average values of microscopic quantities over such physically infinitesimal regions can thus be treated as continuous space-time functions; the averaging process has the result of smoothing out the irregular fluctuations of the microscopic quantities.

The fundamental problem of the theory of electrons can now be stated as follows: from the equations (1) for the microscopic electromagnetic field due to a given assembly of atomic systems, the equations satisfied by the averaged field quantities are to be derived and their relation to the equations of ordinary electromagnetic theory established. This last problem will involve the interpretation of the averaged fields in terms of the macroscopic quantities which occur in Maxwell's theory, viz. the electric and magnetic field intensities and polarization densities. The scope of this theory is of course restricted to slowly varying fields. In addition, there is the domain of optical phenomena, in which field variations of microscopic order give rise to directly observable effects; we shall therefore have to show separately how the optical properties of matter can be deduced from our fundamental assumptions.

The macroscopic field intensities are defined by the forces they exert on suitable test bodies. Likewise, the microscopic equations (1) must be supplemented by a specification of the dynamical actions of the microscopic field variables on the charges and currents. This is done by introducing a density of force $\mathbf{f}$ by the relation

$$\mathbf{f} = \varrho\,\mathbf{e} + \mathbf{i} \wedge \mathbf{h} = \varrho\,\mathbf{e} + \varrho\,\frac{\mathbf{v}}{c} \wedge \mathbf{h}, \qquad (2)$$

which expresses how the field **e**, **h** acts on the charge ϱ and current **i** contained in a unit volume. From the point of view of atomic theory, this expression for the *Lorentz force*, as it is called, must be considered as an additional hypothesis, independent of the equations (1). Just as in statistical mechanics, the idea is to introduce for the microscopic quantities fundamental laws of the same form as the known relations between the corresponding macroscopic quantities, and to justify these hypotheses by showing that they imply the macroscopic laws. In the theory of electrons the complete set of basic assumptions consists of (*a*) the laws of motion of the charges, (*b*) the equations (1) governing the production of electromagnetic fields by the charges and currents, and finally (*c*) the expression (2) for the Lorentz force, which defines the dynamical action of the fields on the charges and currents.

For later use we note here that the charge and current densities satisfy the so-called *equation of continuity*,

$$\frac{\partial \varrho}{\partial \tau} + \operatorname{div} \mathbf{i} = 0. \tag{3}$$

This equation, which expresses the conservation of electric charge, is a direct consequence of the fundamental relations (1).

2. AVERAGING OVER PHYSICALLY INFINITESIMAL REGIONS

Let us consider any point of space P (with co-ordinates x, y, z) and any instant τ, and let us surround them by a physically infinitesimal volume V and time-interval T. For any microscopic quantity $G(P', \tau')$ we define the corresponding average quantity $\overline{G}(P, \tau)$ by

$$\overline{G}(P, \tau) = \frac{1}{V \cdot T} \int\limits_{V} dv' \int\limits_{T} d\tau' \, G(P', \tau'). \tag{4}$$

In this formula P or P' is an abbreviation for the set of spatial co-ordinates x, y, z or x', y', z' and dv' denotes the volume element $dx' \, dy' \, dz'$. If we let V and T tend to zero while always enclosing the point P and instant τ respectively, we obtain the average $\overline{G}(P, \tau)$ as a continuous function of its arguments. Strictly speaking, this passage to the limit is not allowed by the physical meaning underlying the averaging process; but it does exactly correspond to the kind of idealization which characterizes the macroscopic description of the phenomena.

The fundamental property of the averages defined by (4) can be expressed briefly by saying that *differentiation and averaging may be interchanged*. This means, precisely:

$$\frac{\partial \overline{G}(P,\tau)}{\partial x} = \frac{1}{V \cdot T} \int_V dv' \int_T d\tau' \frac{\partial G(P',\tau')}{\partial x'} = \overline{\frac{\partial G}{\partial x}}, \tag{5}$$

and similar relations for the variables y, z, τ instead of x. By means of formulae like (5), the averages of the derivatives of microscopic quantities can at once be evaluated in terms of the averages of these quantities themselves.

The proof is very simple. We replace the integration variables P', τ' with new variables P'', τ'' by means of

$$P' = P + P'' \quad \text{and} \quad \tau' = \tau + \tau'';$$

this leaves the element of space-time $dv' \, d\tau'$ unaltered in form, i.e. $= dv'' \, d\tau''$, while

$$\frac{\partial G(P',\tau')}{\partial x'} = \frac{\partial G(P+P'',\tau+\tau'')}{\partial x}.$$

Therefore,

$$\frac{1}{V \cdot T} \int_V dv' \int_T d\tau' \frac{\partial G(P',\tau')}{\partial x'} = \frac{1}{V \cdot T} \frac{\partial}{\partial x} \int_V dv'' \int_T d\tau'' \, G(P+P'', \tau+\tau'')$$

$$= \frac{\partial}{\partial x} \overline{G}(P,\tau).$$

3. IDENTIFICATION OF THE ELECTROMAGNETIC FIELD AVERAGES

If we take the average on both sides of each of the fundamental equations (1) and eliminate the averages of derivatives with the help of the relations (5), we get immediately

$$\operatorname{curl} \overline{\mathbf{h}} = \overline{\mathbf{i}} + \frac{\partial \overline{\mathbf{e}}}{\partial \tau}, \quad \operatorname{curl} \overline{\mathbf{e}} = -\frac{\partial \overline{\mathbf{h}}}{\partial \tau}$$

$$\operatorname{div} \overline{\mathbf{e}} = \overline{\varrho} \quad , \quad \operatorname{div} \overline{\mathbf{h}} = 0. \tag{6}$$

The equations of the second column, which do not involve the charges and currents, may be compared with the corresponding equations of Maxwell's theory,

$$\text{curl } \mathbf{E} = -\frac{\partial \mathbf{B}}{\partial \tau}, \qquad \text{div } \mathbf{B} = 0, \qquad (7)$$

involving the electric field intensity $\mathbf{E}$ and magnetic induction $\mathbf{B}$. This suggests the identification

$$\bar{\mathbf{e}} = \mathbf{E}, \qquad \bar{\mathbf{h}} = \mathbf{B}, \qquad (8)$$

which gives the interpretation of the averaged microscopic field variables in terms of the macroscopic quantities of Maxwell's theory.

The remaining set of equations (6) becomes

$$\text{curl } \mathbf{B} = \bar{\mathbf{i}} + \frac{\partial \mathbf{E}}{\partial \tau}, \qquad \text{div } \mathbf{E} = \bar{\varrho}, \qquad (9)$$

and our main task is now to evaluate the average densities of charge and current.

4.   THE AVERAGE CHARGE DENSITY

Since atoms are electrically neutral, it seems at first sight that only ions can contribute to the average charge density $\bar{\varrho}$. This ionic contribution corresponds to what is called in Maxwell's theory the *true* charge density ϱ_t, which only occurs in conducting media. We have seen in Chapter I how the nature of the ions participating in electrolytic and gaseous conduction has been ascertained. To complete the picture, we may add that metallic conduction is due to electrons moving freely in the metal; they are kept within the metal by a "potential barrier" at the boundary, due to the attraction of the positive ions which form the rigid metallic lattice.

In dielectrics, however, there is according to Maxwell's theory another contribution to the charge density, the so-called *free* charges, which only appear in regions of inhomogeneity, e.g. at the surface of discontinuity separating two different dielectrics. In our atomic picture we shall therefore look for the origin of the

free charge density in changes of the density of the distribution of
the atoms (or molecules) at the boundary of two adjacent volume
elements. In fact, if we imagine for a moment the whole charge of
each atom concentrated at some point of the interior of the atom,
there will be no average charge density; if we then restore the
original charge distribution by moving each charge element back
to the point which it actually occupies, this will make no difference
so far as the atoms situated entirely within the boundaries of a
physically infinitesimal volume element are concerned; but if an
atom is cut by the boundary of this volume element, part of the
charge will remain in this volume element, while the rest will
contribute to the charge contained in the adjacent volume element.
If the distribution of the atoms is uniform, this boundary effect
will of course again cancel on the average, but if there is an inhomogeneity in the distribution of the atoms a net effect will
result, which is just the free charge density.

Let us follow this argument quantitatively. We may obviously
disregard all variations of charge density with time and only
consider space averages. The "position" of an atom will be fixed
by that of some interior point P, to which we refer the position
of any other point P_a of the atom by means of the radius vector $\mathbf{r}_a$
joining P to P_a. We must allow the charge density to depend not
only on $\mathbf{r}_a$ but also explicitly on the position of the atom: such a
dependence arises, for example, if the charge distribution in the
atom is influenced by some external field slowly varying in space.
In order to avoid unessential complications in the following
argument we shall begin with the particular case in which all atoms
in the same physically infinitesimal volume element (in which any
external influence may be regarded as constant) have the same
orientation in space, i.e. can be made to coincide by a simple
translation. Once this case is treated it will be easy to generalize
the result for any distribution of atoms. Let dS be a physically
infinitesimal surface element at point P, separating two adjacent
volume elements in which the number of atoms $N(P')$ per unit
volume is supposed to vary from point to point; of course, this
atomic density $N(P')$ is of the type of the macroscopic quantities:

its spatial variation is "slow", i.e. continuous on our physically infinitesimal scale. Consider an atom situated at a point P' in the neighbourhood of the boundary dS, and imagine the whole charge to have been concentrated at P'. Let us fix our attention on an element of charge $\varrho(P', \mathbf{r}_a) \, dv_a$ of this atom, actually situated at a point P_a. If the vector $\mathbf{r}_a$ crosses the surface dS, the corresponding charge $\varrho(P', \mathbf{r}_a) \, dv_a$, when brought back to its original position, will be lost to the volume element in which P' is situated. We have to add all similar contributions to the charge crossing the surface dS for all atoms along this surface in the adjacent volume elements. In order to perform this summation we first keep the radius vector $\mathbf{r}_a$ fixed and add up the contributions $\varrho(P', \mathbf{r}_a) \, dv_a$ from all atoms; then we integrate over the volume of the atom.

For a given $\mathbf{r}_a$ there are equal contributions $\varrho(P', \mathbf{r}_a) \, dv_a$ from all the atoms contained in a cylinder of base dS whose height is the projection of $\mathbf{r}_a$ on the normal (defined by a unit vector $\mathbf{n}$) to dS at P. Denoting by $\mathbf{r}_a^0$ the unit vector in the direction of $\mathbf{r}_a$, and by r' the distance measured from the base in this direction, we write for the charge transported across dS over the distance and in the direction specified by $\mathbf{r}_a$

$$dS \cdot dv_a \cdot \mathbf{n} \cdot \mathbf{r}_a^0 \int_0^{r_a} dr' \, \varrho(P', \mathbf{r}_a) \, N(P'), \qquad (10)$$

r_a being the length of the vector $\mathbf{r}_a$. The slowly varying function ϱN may be replaced by the first terms of its Taylor expansion at P:

$$\varrho(P', \mathbf{r}_a) \, N(P') = \varrho(P, \mathbf{r}_a) \, N(P) - r' \, (\mathbf{r}_a^0 \cdot \operatorname{grad}_P \varrho N) + \dots; \quad (11)$$

the minus sign in the second term arises from the fact that the unit vector $\mathbf{r}_a^0$ points from P' towards P, whereas we need the vector PP' pointing in the opposite direction. Inserting (11) in (10) and integrating over the volume of the atom, we get

$$\sigma_f dS = dS \, [\mathbf{n} \cdot \int_{\text{atom}} dv_a \, \mathbf{r}_a \varrho(P, \mathbf{r}_a) \cdot N(P)$$

$$- \tfrac{1}{2} \, \mathbf{n} \cdot \int_{\text{atom}} dv_a \, \mathbf{r}_a \, (\mathbf{r}_a \cdot \operatorname{grad}_P \varrho N)]. \qquad (12)$$

This is the net charge which crosses the surface element dS, in the direction indicated by the vector $\mathbf{n}$, when the charge distribution in the atoms is restored. If the element dS belongs to a physical surface of discontinuity it represents the "free charge" appearing on this surface element; the quantity σ_f defined by (12) is in this case the superficial density of free charge. In order to treat the more general case of spatial inhomogeneity, i.e. to calculate the free charge $\varrho_f\,dv$ contained in a physically infinitesimal volume element dv, we have just to integrate the expression (12) over the whole boundary of the volume element, the transport of charge being at each point taken in the *inward* direction. The space density of free charge is thus defined by

$$\varrho_f = -\frac{1}{dv} \int\limits_{\substack{\text{boundary} \\ \text{of } dv}} \sigma_f\,dS, \tag{13}$$

if, as usual, the unit normal vector $\mathbf{n}$ is chosen pointing outwards.

Formula (12) involves the structure of the atom through a series of quantities of tensor character, the *electric multipole moments*, of which we have only written out the first two:

$$\mathbf{p}(P) = \int\limits_{\text{atom}} dv_a\,\mathbf{r}_a\,\varrho(P,\mathbf{r}_a), \tag{14}$$

$$\mathbf{q}(P) = \tfrac{1}{2} \int\limits_{\text{atom}} dv_a\,\mathbf{r}_a\mathbf{r}_a\,\varrho(P,\mathbf{r}_a); \tag{15}$$

for the tensor (15) Gibbs' dyadic notation is used, as explained in the Appendix With this notation we may write (12) in the form

$$\sigma_f\,dS = dS\,\mathbf{n} \cdot [\mathbf{p}\,N - \text{Div}\,(\mathbf{q}\,N)]. \tag{16}$$

It will be observed that the order of magnitude of the successive terms in the expansion giving $\sigma_f\,dS$ decreases very rapidly. Let us denote by a the order of magnitude of atomic linear dimensions, and by l that of the distances over which the variations of macroscopic quantities become appreciable: we see that each successive step in the expansion involves a factor a/l in the order of magnitude of the corresponding multipole moment.

The first coefficient $\mathbf{p}$ is the *electric dipole moment* of the atom. This name will be easily understood if we observe that without changing anything of the state of the atom we may attach to the extremity P of each radius vector $\mathbf{r}_a$ a charge $-\varrho(P, \mathbf{r}_a)\, dv_a$ equal and opposite to that attached to its other extremity P_a: in fact, the total charge $-\int_{\text{atom}} \varrho(P, \mathbf{r}_a)\, dv_a$ added at P vanishes. The quantity $\mathbf{p}$ then obviously appears as the vector sum of all the dipoles formed in this way. The argument shows also that the definition of $\mathbf{p}$ is independent of the choice of the origin P of the radii vectores $\mathbf{r}_a$. The next coefficient $\mathbf{q}$ is the *electric quadrupole moment*. It can likewise be pictured as referring to pairs of elementary dipoles with parallel axes and opposite signs. More generally, the nth coefficient in the expansion for $\sigma_f\, dS$, which is a tensor of order n, is called for the same reason the *electric 2^n-pole moment*. The successive electric multipole moments give an increasingly detailed picture of the charge distribution in the atom; for most purposes, however, the dipole moment suffices.

In the case (hitherto assumed) of atoms of identical orientation we can pass immediately from the multipole moments of single atoms to the corresponding macroscopic densities of such moments. Thus,

$$\mathbf{P}(P) = \mathbf{p}(P)\, N(P), \tag{17}$$

$$\mathbf{Q}(P) = \mathbf{q}(P)\, N(P) \tag{18}$$

represent the respective densities of *electric polarization* and electric quadrupole moment. In the general case of atoms of different spatial orientations we have simply to divide them into groups corresponding to the same orientation (or to orientations comprised in an elementary solid angle) and apply the preceding argument to each group separately. Instead of (17) and (18) we then get for the macroscopic densities formulae of the type

$$\mathbf{P}(P) = \sum_\theta \mathbf{p}_\theta(P)\, N_\theta(P), \tag{19}$$

$$\mathbf{Q}(P) = \sum_\theta \mathbf{q}_\theta(P)\, N_\theta(P), \tag{20}$$

where $\sum\limits_{\theta}$ denotes a summation or an integration over the spatial orientations symbolized by the index θ. In the following we shall in general work with the simpler expressions of the form (17), (18) without mentioning the obvious generalizations (19), (20). In terms of macroscopic densities formula (16) thus takes the form

$$\sigma_f \, dS = dS \, \mathbf{n} \cdot (\mathbf{P} - \mathrm{Div} \, \mathbf{Q}). \tag{21}$$

Inserting this in (13), we get by Gauss' theorem

$$\varrho_f = - \, \mathrm{div} \, (\mathbf{P} - \mathrm{Div} \, \mathbf{Q}). \tag{22}$$

Summarizing, we have obtained for the average charge density

$$\bar{\varrho} = \varrho_t + \varrho_f = \varrho_t - \mathrm{div} \, (\mathbf{P} - \mathrm{Div} \, \mathbf{Q}). \tag{23}$$

Inserting this expression in the second equation (9), we may write this equation in the Maxwellian form

$$\mathrm{div} \, \mathbf{D} = \varrho_t \tag{24}$$

by introducing the electric displacement

$$\mathbf{D} = \mathbf{E} + \mathbf{P} - \mathrm{Div} \, \mathbf{Q}. \tag{25}$$

This definition differs from that generally used in Maxwell's theory by the occurrence of the quadrupole term, which is ordinarily neglected, as well as the further terms arising from the higher multipole moments.

5. THE AVERAGE CURRENT DENSITY

The evaluation of the average current density proceeds along similar lines to that of the average charge density, with characteristic differences. We will now also take into consideration slow variations in time of the external fields, and accordingly treat the charge and current densities as functions of τ as well as of the position P of the atom and the radius vector $\mathbf{r}_a$. We are only interested, of course, in the *slow* variation of these quantities with respect to τ, and we should always smooth out their rapid fluctuations by averaging. Since, however, such time-averages do not change the form of the expressions to which they are applied, they will be left out from all following calculations. In order to achieve full generality we ought to consider also slow time-variations of the distribution of the atoms; but for the sake of simplicity we shall confine ourselves to stationary distributions, characterized by a spatial function $N(P)$. The density of conduction current I_c is then entirely attributable to ionic convection.

Besides this term arising from the ions, there is a first contribution from neutral atoms to the average current density even when their distribution is uniform, since, in contrast to $\int_{\text{atom}} \varrho(P, \tau, r_a) \, dv_a$, the integral $\int_{\text{atom}} i(P, \tau, r_a) \, dv_a$ does not in general vanish. This contribution is

$$I_p = N(P) \int_{\text{atom}} i(P, \tau, r_a) \, dv_a. \tag{26}$$

A last contribution I_m arises from the spatial inhomogeneity of the atomic distribution in a way entirely analogous to the free charge density:

$$I_m = - \frac{1}{dv} \int_{\substack{\text{boundary} \\ \text{of } dv}} dS \cdot N(P) \int_{\text{atom}} i(P, \tau, r_a) \, (n \cdot r_a) \, dv_a. \tag{27}$$

It is consistent here to limit the Taylor expansion of the atomic distribution $N(P)$ to its first term, since this term is already of the order of magnitude of the electric quadrupole terms which are the last we have retained in the previous calculations. In order to see this we may take as a measure for "macroscopic" times (analogous to the length l introduced in the preceding section when discussing orders of magnitude of multipole moments) the period of an electromagnetic wave of wave-length l; since this period is also that of the moving charges in the atoms, we have for the atomic velocities $v/c \approx a/l$. Therefore the terms of the expansion occurring in (27), which are obtained by replacing ϱ by $i = \varrho v/c$ in the expression (12), (13) for ϱ_f, are all one order of magnitude smaller than those occurring in the latter expression.

Collecting the various contributions just discussed, we have for the average current density

$$\bar{\mathbf{i}} = \mathbf{I}_c + \mathbf{I}_p + \mathbf{I}_m. \tag{28}$$

We proceed with the transformation of the two last terms into expressions more readily interpretable. In the first place, it follows from the continuity equation (3) that

$$\int_{\text{atom}} \mathbf{r}_a \frac{\partial \varrho}{\partial \tau}\, dv_a = - \int_{\text{atom}} \mathbf{r}_a \operatorname{div} \mathbf{i}\, dv_a,$$

the divergence being taken with respect to the point P_a, while the point P is kept fixed. The left-hand side is just $\partial \mathbf{p}/\partial \tau$; transforming the right-hand side by partial integration, we get

$$\frac{\partial \mathbf{p}}{\partial \tau} = \int_{\text{atom}} \mathbf{i}\, dv_a. \tag{29}$$

Taking account of (29) and (17), formula (26) takes the simple form

$$\mathbf{I}_p = \frac{\partial \mathbf{P}}{\partial \tau}. \tag{30}$$

The expression (27) for $\mathbf{I}_m$ contains the dyadic tensor $\int_{\text{atom}} \mathbf{i} \mathbf{r}_a\, dv_a$, which may be decomposed into a symmetrical and an antisymmetrical part. The former, as we shall show, is just the time derivative of the electric quadrupole moment; the latter involves a new physical quantity related to the current distribution in the atom. We start again from the continuity equation (3) but multiply it now by $(\mathbf{n} \cdot \mathbf{r}_a)\, \mathbf{r}_a$ before integrating over the atom:

$$\int_{\text{atom}} (\mathbf{n} \cdot \mathbf{r}_a)\, \mathbf{r}_a \frac{\partial \varrho}{\partial \tau}\, dv_a = - \int_{\text{atom}} (\mathbf{n} \cdot \mathbf{r}_a)\, \mathbf{r}_a \operatorname{div} \mathbf{i}\, dv_a. \tag{31}$$

The left-hand side is easily expressed in terms of the electric quadrupole moment (15) as the vector

$$2\, \mathbf{n} \cdot \frac{\partial \mathbf{q}}{\partial \tau}.$$

The right-hand side is further transformed as follows: one has

$$(\mathbf{n} \cdot \mathbf{r}_a) \operatorname{div} \mathbf{i} = \operatorname{div} \{(\mathbf{n} \cdot \mathbf{r}_a)\, \mathbf{i}\} - \mathbf{i} \cdot \operatorname{grad} (\mathbf{n} \cdot \mathbf{r}_a)$$
$$= \operatorname{div} \{(\mathbf{n} \cdot \mathbf{r}_a)\, \mathbf{i}\} - \mathbf{i} \cdot \mathbf{n};$$

therefore, with a partial integration,

$$-\int_{\text{atom}} (\mathbf{n} \cdot \mathbf{r}_a)\, \mathbf{r}_a \operatorname{div} \mathbf{i}\, dv_a = \int_{\text{atom}} \{(\mathbf{n} \cdot \mathbf{r}_a)\, \mathbf{i} + (\mathbf{n} \cdot \mathbf{i})\, \mathbf{r}_a\}\, dv_a.$$

The result of this calculation (in which $\mathbf{n}$ plays the part of an arbitrary vector) may be written in tensor form:

$$\frac{1}{2} \int_{\text{atom}} (\mathbf{i}\, \mathbf{r}_a + \mathbf{r}_a\, \mathbf{i})\, dv_a = \frac{\partial \mathbf{q}}{\partial \tau}. \qquad (32)$$

The antisymmetrical part of the tensor is readily transformed by observing that

$$\frac{1}{2} \int_{\text{atom}} \{(\mathbf{n} \cdot \mathbf{r}_a)\, \mathbf{i} - (\mathbf{n} \cdot \mathbf{i})\, \mathbf{r}_a\}\, dv_a = \frac{1}{2} \int_{\text{atom}} (\mathbf{r}_a \wedge \mathbf{i}) \wedge \mathbf{n}\, dv_a = \mu \wedge \mathbf{n}, \qquad (33)$$

with the notation

$$\mu = \frac{1}{2} \int_{\text{atom}} \mathbf{r}_a \wedge \mathbf{i}\, dv_a. \qquad (34)$$

Combining (32) and (33), we finally get

$$\int_{\text{atom}} (\mathbf{n} \cdot \mathbf{r}_a)\, \mathbf{i}\, dv_a = -\mathbf{n} \wedge \mu + \mathbf{n} \cdot \frac{\partial \mathbf{q}}{\partial \tau}. \qquad (35)$$

The quantity μ is a new atomic parameter of simple physical interpretation. Observing that $\mathbf{i}\, dv_a$ represents what is called in electrodynamics an "element of current", and remembering Ampère's law on the equivalence of a closed linear current and a magnetic sheet, we recognize in the quantity μ the total *magnetic dipole moment* due to the current distribution in the atom. It is the first member of a series of *magnetic multipole moments* similar to that of the electric multipole moments. The corresponding macroscopic density

$$\mathbf{M} = N \mu \qquad (36)$$

is the *density of magnetization*.

With (35), (36) and (18) the expression (27) for $\mathbf{I}_m$ becomes

$$\mathbf{I}_m = \frac{1}{dv} \int\limits_{\substack{\text{boundary}\\\text{of } dv}} dS \left(\mathbf{n} \wedge \mathbf{M} - \mathbf{n} \cdot \frac{\partial \mathbf{Q}}{\partial \tau} \right).$$

By corrolaries of Gauss' theorem, the surface integrals can be written

$$\int dS \cdot \mathbf{n} \wedge \mathbf{M} = dv \cdot \operatorname{curl} \mathbf{M},$$

$$\int dS \cdot \mathbf{n} \cdot \frac{\partial \mathbf{Q}}{\partial \tau} = dv \cdot \frac{\partial}{\partial \tau} \operatorname{Div} \mathbf{Q}.$$

Therefore,

$$\mathbf{I}_m = \operatorname{curl} \mathbf{M} - \frac{\partial}{\partial \tau} \operatorname{Div} \mathbf{Q}. \qquad (37)$$

Inserting the results (30) and (37) in (28), we finally obtain for the average current density

$$\bar{\mathbf{i}} = \mathbf{I}_c + \frac{\partial}{\partial \tau} (\mathbf{P} - \operatorname{Div} \mathbf{Q}) + \operatorname{curl} \mathbf{M}. \qquad (38)$$

Comparing the formulae (23) and (38) for the average charge and current densities, we observe that the continuity equation is satisfied separately by the ionic terms $\mathbf{I}_c$, ϱ_t, by the terms depending on the electric multipoles, and by the magnetic term of current density (which, being divergence-free, has no corresponding charge density contribution). If we take into account the definition (25) of the electric displacement and introduce the magnetic field intensity by the definition

$$\mathbf{H} = \mathbf{B} - \mathbf{M}, \qquad (39)$$

we can also put the first equation (9) in the Maxwellian form

$$\operatorname{curl} \mathbf{H} = \mathbf{I}_c + \frac{\partial \mathbf{D}}{\partial \tau}, \qquad (40)$$

which completes the derivation of Maxwell's equations from the premises of the theory of electrons.

The lack of symmetry between our equations (20) and (39) expressing the analogous relations between **D**, **E** on the one hand and **B**, **H** on the other is of course only apparent: there would be complete symmetry if we wrote down in full the series of terms due to all electric or magnetic multipole moments. If, however, we stop these series (as we have done) at a certain order of magnitude, there will always be one term fewer in the magnetic group.

6. CONCLUSION

The chief result of the preceding analysis is to show how the quantities — electric and magnetic polarization — which in Maxwell's equations represent the main influence of material bodies on electromagnetic phenomena are related to structural properties of the atoms expressed by their electric and magnetic dipole moments. We have also seen how the usual form of Maxwell's theory can in principle be completed by considering the effect of higher multipole moments; but these small effects will not be discussed further in the following.

Our remaining task is to investigate how atomic systems, either spontaneously or under the influence of external fields and of their mutual interactions, will give rise to electric and magnetic polarization. In other words, we have to trace the atomic origin of the relations between fields and polarizations treated as empirical expressions in Maxwell's theory. This involves in particular a theory of such parameters as the electric and magnetic susceptibilities and, in optics, the refractive index and absorption coefficient, the aim of such a theory being to express these parameters in terms of atomic properties. In order to solve these problems we must first examine in detail how the atomic charges and currents are acted upon and modified by electromagnetic fields: this will be the subject of the next chapter. It is here that we shall make use for the first time of our fundamental assumption (2), giving the expression for the Lorentz force.

CHAPTER III

DYNAMICAL PROPERTIES OF SYSTEMS OF CHARGED PARTICLES

1. SYSTEMS OF CHARGED PARTICLES

The study of the behaviour of atomic systems under the influence of external fields could be carried out by the same method as in the preceding chapter, i.e. by describing such systems as arbitrary distributions of charges and currents. It is more convenient, however, for this purpose to consider them as systems of charged particles and to treat the motion of these particles under the action of the Lorentz forces by the ordinary methods of point dynamics. It is important to realize the essential difference between the two modes of description. When we specify the system by charge and current densities $\varrho(P_a, \tau)$, $\mathbf{i}(P_a, \tau)$, the space co-ordinates $\mathbf{r}_a$ and the time τ are independent variables, and the motions of the system are contained in the time variations of the functions ϱ, $\mathbf{i}$. If we regard the system as composed of charged particles, with charges e_k ($k = 1, 2, \ldots$), the space co-ordinates $\mathbf{x}_k$ of these particles are functions of the time, giving directly an account of their motion; the velocities $\mathbf{v}_k \equiv \dot{\mathbf{x}}_k$ define the corresponding current *intensities* $e_k \mathbf{v}_k/c$. The passage from one mode of description to the other is readily effected by relations of the type

$$\int_{\text{atom}} \varrho(P_a, \tau)\, F(\mathbf{r}_a)\, dv_a \to \sum_k e_k\, F(\mathbf{x}_k),$$

$$\int_{\text{atom}} \mathbf{i}(P_a, \tau)\, F(\mathbf{r}_a)\, dv_a \to \sum_k \frac{e_k}{c}\, \mathbf{v}_k\, F(\mathbf{x}_k). \tag{1}$$

In particular, from the density of the Lorentz force defined by our fundamental assumption (II, 2), it follows that the force acting on the kth particle of the system is given by

$$\mathbf{F}_k = e_k\, \mathbf{E}(\mathbf{x}_k) + \frac{e_k}{c}\, \mathbf{v}_k \wedge \mathbf{H}(\mathbf{x}_k). \tag{2}$$

2. THE LAGRANGIAN AND HAMILTONIAN

The fact that the Lorentz force defined by (2) depends on the velocity of the particle raises the problem of how to extend to this type of force the formalism of Lagrange's and Hamilton's equations. The possibility of such an extension is established by proving that *if L_0 denotes the Lagrangian of a free particle, the Lagrangian for this particle moving in a field defined by the vector potential $\mathbf{A}$ and the scalar potential φ is given by $L = L_0 + L_f$ with*

$$L_f = \frac{e}{c}\,\mathbf{v}\cdot\mathbf{A} - e\,\varphi. \tag{3}$$

To show this we have only to verify that the Lagrange equations constructed by means of L yield the Lorentz force. In other words, the expression

$$F_x = -\left\{ \frac{d}{dt}\left(\frac{\partial L_f}{\partial v_x} \right) - \frac{\partial L_f}{\partial x} \right\}$$

must reduce to the corresponding component of the Lorentz force

$$e\,E_x + \frac{e}{c}\,(\mathbf{v}\wedge\mathbf{H})_x.$$

Indeed,

$$\partial L_f / \partial v_x = (e/c)\,A_x$$

and

$$\frac{dA_x}{dt} = \frac{\partial A_x}{\partial t} + v_x \frac{\partial A_x}{\partial x} + v_y \frac{\partial A_x}{\partial y} + v_z \frac{\partial A_x}{\partial z};$$

further,

$$\frac{c}{e}\frac{\partial L_f}{\partial x} = -c\frac{\partial\varphi}{\partial x} + v_x \frac{\partial A_x}{\partial x} + v_y \frac{\partial A_y}{\partial x} + v_z \frac{\partial A_z}{\partial x};$$

therefore,

$$F_x = e\left(-\frac{\partial\varphi}{\partial x} - \frac{\partial A_x}{\partial \tau} \right) + \frac{e}{c}\,(v_y \operatorname{curl}_z \mathbf{A} - v_z \operatorname{curl}_y \mathbf{A}),$$

which is the desired result.

The transition from the Lagrangian to the Hamiltonian leads to a very simple and elegant conclusion: *if $H_0(\mathbf{k})$ is the Hamiltonian of* *a free particle of momentum* **k**, *the Hamiltonian of this particle in the external field defined by the potentials* **A**, φ *is*

$$H = H_0\!\left(\mathbf{k} - \frac{e}{c}\,\mathbf{A}\right) + e\,\varphi; \qquad (4)$$

i.e. the Hamiltonian H is built up of a "kinetic" term, which is the same function of the arguments $\mathbf{k} - (e/c)\mathbf{A}$ as the function of the momenta representing the Hamiltonian H_0 in the absence of field, and a term of "potential" energy defined by the scalar potential of the field.

In order to prove this property, let us first recall that the Hamiltonian H_0 of a free particle of velocity $\mathbf{v}_0$ and momentum $\mathbf{k}_0$ is defined by

$$H_0(\mathbf{k}_0) = \mathbf{k}_0 \cdot \mathbf{v}_0(\mathbf{k}_0) - L_0\{\mathbf{v}_0(\mathbf{k}_0)\},$$

where $\mathbf{v}_0$, as a function of $\mathbf{k}_0$, is obtained by solving the equations which define the components of $\mathbf{k}_0$:

$$k_{0x} = \frac{\partial L_0}{\partial v_{0x}}, \ \ldots$$

Applied to the Lagrangian $L = L_0 + L_f$, the same procedure first gives for the momentum components

$$k_x = \frac{\partial L_0}{\partial v_x} + \frac{e}{c}\,A_x, \ldots,$$

which means that the velocity $\mathbf{v}$ bears the same relation to $\mathbf{k} - (e/c)\mathbf{A}$ as $\mathbf{v}_0$ to $\mathbf{k}_0$. Writing the Hamiltonian as

$$H(\mathbf{k}) = \left(\mathbf{k} - \frac{e}{c}\,\mathbf{A}\right) \cdot \mathbf{v}(\mathbf{k}) + \frac{e}{c}\,\mathbf{A} \cdot \mathbf{v}(\mathbf{k}) - L_0\{\mathbf{v}(\mathbf{k})\} - L_f,$$

with L_f given by (3), we immediately see that it has indeed the form (4).

As regards the free particle functions L_0 and H_0, we recall here their relativistic expressions

$$L_0 = -mc^2 \sqrt{\left(1 - \frac{v^2}{c^2}\right)}, \qquad H_0 = c\,\sqrt{(m^2c^2 + k^2)},$$

$$\text{with} \quad \mathbf{k} = \frac{m\mathbf{v}}{\sqrt{\{1 - (v/c)^2\}}}, \qquad (5)$$

and the non-relativistic approximations (leaving out a constant term mc^2)

$$L_0 = \tfrac{1}{2}\, mv^2, \qquad H_0 = \frac{1}{2m}\, k^2,$$

$$\text{with} \quad \mathbf{k} = m\mathbf{v}. \tag{6}$$

3. SYSTEM IN SLOWLY VARYING EXTERNAL FIELD

Let us consider more particularly the energy of a system of charged particles in a slowly varying external field. A *slowly varying* field is characterized by the condition that the order of magnitude of all space and time derivatives of potential and field components fulfil relations of the type

$$\frac{1}{\varphi}\,\frac{\partial \varphi}{\partial x}\, a \approx \frac{a}{l}. \tag{7}$$

In the case of an external electric field, defined in terms of a scalar potential φ by $\mathbf{E} = -\,\mathrm{grad}\ \varphi$, we have a *potential energy*

$$V = \sum_k e_k\, \varphi(\mathbf{x}_k). \tag{8}$$

If the potential is slowly varying, we may expand it with respect to some arbitrary origin O. Denoting the value of any function at the origin by an index O, we may thus write

$$V = \sum_k e_k\, \varphi_O + \sum_k e_k\, \mathbf{x}_k \cdot (\mathrm{grad}\ \varphi)_O + \ldots$$

The first term is the product of the total charge by the potential at O: it corresponds to the crudest approximation, in which the system is reduced to a charge $\sum_k e_k$ concentrated at O; for a neutral system this term vanishes. In the next term there appears the dipole moment of the system and the field at O; and the following terms of the expansion will involve the successive multipole moments with derivatives of corresponding order of the field. Retaining only the dipole term, we have for a neutral system the potential energy

$$V = -\,\mathbf{p} \cdot \mathbf{E}_O. \tag{9}$$

We shall now treat the case of an external magnetic field, given by the vector potential **A**, assuming for simplicity the non-relativistic expression (6) for the Hamiltonian. According to (4) we may write, for the energy of one particle,

$$H = \frac{1}{2m}\,\mathbf{k}^2 - \frac{\mathbf{k}}{m}\cdot\frac{e}{c}\,\mathbf{A} + \frac{e^2}{2\,mc^2}\,\mathbf{A}^2.$$

If the magnetic field can be regarded as a small perturbation, the first term represents the kinetic energy of the motion of the particle as it would be determined by the stronger non-magnetic forces acting on it; the other terms embody the additional energy, also of a "kinetic" nature, resulting from the action of the magnetic field defined by **A**. We shall in the next section analyse more closely how this energy arises; now we are concerned with its evaluation. For this purpose, it will be advisable to express the momentum in terms of the velocity, by means of the relation $\mathbf{k} = m\mathbf{v} + (e/c)\,\mathbf{A}$, since it is the velocity which enters into the definition of the magnetic multipole moments. We thus get for the magnetic energy K of one particle

$$K = -\frac{e}{c}\,\mathbf{v}\cdot\mathbf{A} - \frac{e^2}{2\,mc^2}\,\mathbf{A}^2. \qquad (10)$$

We have now to expand the vector potential:

$$\mathbf{A}(\mathbf{x}) = \mathbf{A}_0 + \mathbf{x}\cdot\mathrm{Grad}_0\mathbf{A}_0.$$

In order to introduce the magnetic field $\mathbf{H} = \mathrm{curl}\,\mathbf{A}$, we observe that the tensor $\mathrm{Grad}\,\mathbf{A}$ may be decomposed into an antisymmetric part, which involves the axial vector $\frac{1}{2}\,\mathrm{curl}\,\mathbf{A}$, and a symmetric part $(\mathrm{Grad}\,\mathbf{A})_S$ (see the Appendix). We may therefore write

$$\mathbf{A}(\mathbf{x}) = \mathbf{A}_0 - \tfrac{1}{2}\,\mathbf{x}\wedge\mathbf{H}_0 + \mathbf{x}\cdot(\mathrm{Grad}_0\,\mathbf{A}_0)_S. \qquad (11)$$

According to (11), the linear term of the energy K can be decomposed into two parts, K_m and K_e, of which the former is due to the second term of (11) and thus depends on the magnetic field $\mathbf{H}_0$, while the latter, due to the other two terms of (11), refers (as we will show) to the electric field $\mathbf{E}^{\mathrm{ind}} = -\,\partial\mathbf{A}_0/\partial\tau$ induced at O by the magnetic field when the latter varies in time. The contribution

K_m, for any system of charged particles, can immediately be written in terms of the magnetic dipole moment

$$K_m = - \mu \cdot \mathbf{H}_O; \tag{12}$$

although entirely analogous in form to (9), this expression has a quite different physical interpretation, to which we shall return in the next section.

The term K_e involves the electric moments $\mathbf{p}$ and $\mathbf{q}$ of the system of charged particles; in fact, it can be written

$$K_e = - \frac{d\mathbf{p}}{d\tau} \cdot \mathbf{A}_O - \frac{d\mathbf{q}}{d\tau} : \mathrm{Grad}_O \, \mathbf{A}_O.$$

The time average of this expression over a physically infinitesimal time-interval reduces, however, to

$$K_e = - \mathbf{p} \cdot \mathbf{E}^{\mathrm{ind}} - \mathbf{q} : \mathrm{Grad} \, \mathbf{E}^{\mathrm{ind}}, \tag{13}$$

since the average of the remaining time-derivative

$$- \frac{d}{d\tau} \left(\mathbf{p} \cdot \mathbf{A}_O + \mathbf{q} : \mathrm{Grad}_O \, \mathbf{A}_O \right)$$

vanishes. In fact, the macroscopic time-average may be mathematically represented by the limit of a time-average for an infinitely long time-interval. If the function $F(\tau)$ is bounded at all times, it is clear that

$$\lim_{T \to \infty} \frac{1}{T} \int_0^T \frac{dF(\tau)}{d\tau} \, d\tau = \lim_{T \to \infty} \frac{1}{T} \{ F(T) - F(0) \} = 0.$$

The energy K_e has, of course, the general form of an electric interaction energy.

As regards the quadratic term in (10), we shall use it only for a constant magnetic field $\mathbf{H}$; we may then simply replace $\mathbf{A}$ by $- \frac{1}{2} \mathbf{x} \wedge \mathbf{H}$, and we get

$$K_m^{(2)} = - \frac{1}{8} \sum_k \frac{e_k^2}{m_k c^2} s_k^2 \, \mathbf{H}^2, \tag{14}$$

where s_k denotes the distance of the kth particle of the system from an axis parallel to the magnetic field through the origin O with respect to which the multipole moments are defined.

4. LARMOR'S THEOREM

The motion of a system of particles in a sufficiently weak magnetic field can be described very simply in the important case in which all moving particles have the same specific charge. This condition is readily fulfilled if the system is an atom (or atomic ion): the centre of mass practically coincides with the heavy positive nucleus, and we are only concerned with the motion of the electrons with respect to this nucleus. We shall therefore limit the following considerations to *atoms* and place the origin O, to which we refer the motions of the constituent electrons, at the nucleus. The extension of our results to molecules composed of two or more atoms demands great caution; it is only legitimate in so far as the influence of the relative motions of the atomic nuclei can be neglected in comparison with the effect due to the electrons.

The theory of the behaviour of atoms in magnetic fields is contained in *Larmor's theorem* (1897) *, according to which the effect of the magnetic field (provided quadratic terms may be disregarded) is to superpose upon the state of motion existing in the absence of the field a uniform precession of the whole system around the axis of the field passing through the nucleus, with an angular velocity

$$\omega_L = \eta \, \mathbf{H}, \quad \text{with} \quad \eta = -\frac{e}{2mc}. \tag{15}$$

The coefficient η is determined by the specific charge of the moving particles; if these are electrons, η is positive.

To prove Larmor's theorem, we first verify that the state of motion just described is an approximate solution of the mechanical equations in the presence of the magnetic field. Let $\dot{\mathbf{x}}_a$, $\ddot{\mathbf{x}}_a$ be the velocity and acceleration of any particle of the system under the action of the given force $\mathbf{F}_a$ and the Lorentz force due to the

---

* See J. J. Larmor, *Aether and matter* (Cambridge, 1900). This work is a profound and highly original production. Although many problems discussed in it have become obsolete, it is still instructive; it makes hard reading, however. "Larmor's theorem" is discussed in Appendix F (pp. 341 et seq.).

magnetic field; the equations of motion are

$$m\ddot{\mathbf{x}}_a = \mathbf{F}_a + \frac{e}{c}\,\dot{\mathbf{x}}_a \wedge \mathbf{H}\,. \qquad (16)$$

In a system of axes rotating with a constant angular velocity ω, the velocity $\dot{\mathbf{x}}$ and acceleration $\ddot{\mathbf{x}}$ are related to $\dot{\mathbf{x}}_a$, $\ddot{\mathbf{x}}_a$ by

$$\begin{aligned}
\dot{\mathbf{x}}_a &= \dot{\mathbf{x}} + \omega \wedge \mathbf{x}, \\
\ddot{\mathbf{x}}_a &= \ddot{\mathbf{x}} + 2\omega \wedge \dot{\mathbf{x}} + \omega \wedge (\omega \wedge \mathbf{x}).
\end{aligned} \qquad (17)$$

Comparing (16) and (17), and neglecting for a moment quadratic effects, we see that by taking $\omega = \omega_L$ given by (15), the Lorentz force is balanced by the Coriolis force $-2m\omega_L \wedge \dot{\mathbf{x}}$, so that the equations of motion in the rotating system reduce to $m\ddot{\mathbf{x}} = \mathbf{F}_a$. In other words, there is a state of motion in the presence of the magnetic field, characterized, to this approximation, as a super-position of the *Larmor precession* ω_L upon the motion determined by the other forces $\mathbf{F}_a$.

More accurately, after the elimination of the linear terms by the choice $\omega = \omega_L$, the equations of motion in the rotating system become

$$m\ddot{\mathbf{x}} = \mathbf{F}_a + m\,\omega_L \wedge (\omega_L \wedge \mathbf{x}), \qquad (18)$$

i.e. for the component $\mathbf{s}$ of $\mathbf{x}$ perpendicular to the magnetic field,

$$\ddot{\mathbf{s}} + \omega_L^2\,\mathbf{s} = \frac{1}{m}\,\mathbf{F}_{a\perp}\,, \qquad (19)$$

where $\mathbf{F}_{a\perp}$ denotes the component of $\mathbf{F}_a$ in the same direction. If we take for $\mathbf{F}_{a\perp}$ a force of the quasi-elastic type assumed to correspond to the binding of electrons in atomic systems, the acceleration due to this force may be represented by $-\omega_0^2\mathbf{s}$, where ω_0 is of the order of the optical frequencies. Inserting numerical values, we see that the acceleration term $-\omega_L^2\mathbf{s}$ only becomes significant for values of the magnetic field of the order 10^8 gauss: this result gives an idea of the scope of Larmor's theorem. On the other hand, if $\mathbf{F}_a = 0$, i.e. if we consider the deflection of a free particle in a magnetic field, Larmor's theorem obviously breaks down; in fact, it is readily seen that the harmonic oscillation described by (19)

combines with the Larmor precession to give in the plane perpendicular to the magnetic field a circular trajectory described with
a uniform angular velocity of *twice* the Larmor frequency ω_L.
The increase in kinetic energy of the system due to the Larmor
precession is

$$\sum_k \tfrac{1}{2}\, m_k \left\{ (\dot{\mathbf{x}}_k + \omega_L \wedge \mathbf{x}_k)^2 - (\dot{\mathbf{x}}_k)^2 \right\},$$

which may be written, using (17),

$$\sum_k m_k \left\{ \dot{\mathbf{x}}_{ak} \cdot (\omega_L \wedge \mathbf{x}_k) - \tfrac{1}{2}(\omega_L \wedge \mathbf{x}_k)^2 \right\};$$

on account of the definition (15) of ω_L (all specific charges e_k/m_k
being equal), this expression is just the sum $K_m + K_m^{(2)}$ of the
magnetic interaction energy terms derived above and defined by
(12) and (14). The Larmor precession thus offers a precise interpretation of the "kinetic" nature of this magnetic energy.

It now remains to be shown how, on switching on the magnetic
field from zero to its final value **H**, the system actually passes
from its original state of motion to that described by Larmor's
theorem. During this period every charged particle is acted upon,
not only by the increasing magnetic field, but also by the electric
field $- \partial \mathbf{A}/\partial \tau$ induced by it. The magnetic Lorentz force $\dfrac{e}{c}\,\mathbf{v} \wedge \mathbf{H}$ does
not alter the absolute value of the velocity and does not do any
work. The electric force $-\dfrac{e}{c}\dfrac{\partial \mathbf{A}}{\partial t}$ has the effect of bringing the
velocity from its initial value $\mathbf{k}/m$, determined by the other forces
$\mathbf{F}_a$, to its final value $\dfrac{\mathbf{k}}{m} - \dfrac{e}{mc}\mathbf{A}$; the work done by this force is

$$-\frac{e}{c}\int \mathbf{v} \cdot \frac{\partial \mathbf{A}}{\partial t}\, dt = -\frac{e}{mc}\int \mathbf{k} \cdot \frac{\partial \mathbf{A}}{\partial t}\, dt + \frac{e^2}{mc^2}\int \mathbf{A} \cdot \frac{\partial \mathbf{A}}{\partial t}\, dt,$$

the integrals being extended over the period of establishment of
the field. Since the momentum **k** is a rapidly varying function
of the time determined by the atomic forces $\mathbf{F}_a$, it can be replaced in
the first integral on the right-hand side by its time average over
the period considered. As we take the initial value of the vector

potential to be zero, we therefore get for the work done during the establishment of the field

$$- \frac{e}{mc} \mathbf{k} \cdot \mathbf{A} + \frac{e^2}{2mc^2} \mathbf{A}^2,$$

which is just the energy difference (10) between the particle with and without magnetic field. We thus see that provided the switching on of the field is *adiabatic*, i.e. very slow compared to atomic motions, the final state is that described by Larmor's theorem. The most immediate application of Larmor's theorem yields the theory of the normal Zeeman effect. In fact, the Larmor precession directly accounts for the displaced lines, while the second-order effect embodied in equation (19) gives rise to the general frequency shift resulting from the replacement of the proper frequency ω_0 by $\sqrt{(\omega_0^2 + \omega_L^2)}$. This frequency shift, amounting approximately to $\frac{1}{2} \omega_L^2 / \omega_0$, is called the *quadratic Zeeman effect*.

5. MAGNETIC MOMENT AND ANGULAR MOMENTUM

Larmor's theorem expresses a close relation between the magnetic behaviour of atomic systems and rotational motion. Another aspect of this relation becomes apparent when the definition of the magnetic dipole moment of the system is compared with that of its *angular momentum*

$$\mathbf{g} = \sum_k m_k \mathbf{x}_k \wedge \dot{\mathbf{x}}_{ak}. \tag{20}$$

In fact, for atomic systems, i.e. if all moving particles have the same specific charge, we have, with the notation η defined in (15),

$$\mu = - \eta \, \mathbf{g}. \tag{21}$$

The study of the anomalous Zeeman effect and of other properties of atomic spectra has led to the discovery (1925) that an electron does not simply behave like a charged material point; it has also an intrinsic angular momentum, or *spin*, σ, with which an intrinsic magnetic moment μ_s is connected by a relation of the same form as (21) but with a characteristic difference in the coefficient of proportionality:

$$\mu_s = - 2 \eta \, \sigma. \tag{22}$$

The electron spin is a purely quantal effect, which is not susceptible to analysis in classical terms; for our purposes, however, we need only note that *the spin magnetic moment μ_s, when subjected to a magnetic field, can only orient itself in a direction either parallel or antiparallel to the field.*

The spins of the constituent electrons of an atomic system give rise in general to a resultant spin angular momentum $\mathbf{S} = \sum_k \sigma_k$ and a corresponding spin magnetic moment

$$\mu_S = \sum_k \mu_{sk} = -2\eta\mathbf{S}. \tag{23}$$

Owing to the difference of a factor 2 in the coefficients of (21) and (23), there is no general relation of similar simplicity between the total magnetic moment and the total angular momentum $\mathbf{J}$ of the system. For the component μ_J of the total magnetic moment in the direction of $\mathbf{J}$ one may write, however,

$$\mu_J = -g\eta J, \tag{24}$$

where the coefficient

$$g = 1 + \frac{\mathbf{S} \cdot \mathbf{J}}{\mathbf{J}^2} \tag{25}$$

is called the *Landé factor* or *gyromagnetic ratio*. It is the occurrence of this factor in relation (24) which explains the anomalies of the Zeeman effect; only if the total spin $\mathbf{S}$ is zero does (24) reduce to the simple form (21) corresponding to the normal Zeeman effect. A relation of proportionality

$$\mu = -g\eta\mathbf{J} \tag{26}$$

between the total magnetic moment μ and the total angular momentum $\mathbf{J}$ will be valid for those states of the system in which the angular momentum $\mathbf{g}$ and the spin $\mathbf{S}$ are parallel or antiparallel.

6.   THE GYROMAGNETIC EFFECTS

From the proportionality between magnetic moment and angular momentum expressed by (21) or (24) it follows that magnetization of a body is accompanied by an angular momentum, corresponding to a rotation of the body in bulk. Of course, this rotation is in usual circumstances extremely small, but it can be detected by sufficiently sensitive arrangements. Conversely, a bulk rotation imparted to a body will be expected to give rise to a magnetization of this body; also this conclusion has been verified experimentally. In fact, the first successful experiments on these *gyromagnetic effects* were performed at about the same time: the magnetization by rotation was achieved by Barnett in 1914 and the existence of the converse phenomenon was proved by Einstein and de Haas in 1915 *.

The theory of the Barnett effect is quite straightforward. A rotation of angular velocity ω causes a precession of the angular momentum $\mathbf{J}$ of each atom or ion of the body according to the dynamical equation

$$\frac{d\mathbf{J}}{dt} + \omega \wedge \mathbf{J} = 0 .$$

Let us assume (this will suffice for the present discussion) that there is a proportionality relation of the form (26) between the angular momentum and the magnetic moment μ of the atom. The latter quantity will then change according to

$$\frac{d\mu}{dt} + \omega \wedge \mu = 0 .$$

This change can be compared with that which would be produced by a magnetic field $\mathbf{H}$. Such a field exerts a couple $- \mathbf{H} \wedge \mu$ on the atom, which gives rise to a change of angular momentum at the rate

$$\frac{d\mathbf{J}}{dt} = - \mathbf{H} \wedge \mu ,$$

and to an accompanying change of magnetic moment

$$\frac{d\mu}{dt} = + g \eta \; \mathbf{H} \wedge \mu .$$

---

* A review of gyromagnetic effects is given by S. J. Barnett, *Rev. Mod. Phys.*, 7, 129, 1935.

In other words, a rotation ω has the same effect on the magnetization of the body as a magnetic field $\mathbf{H}$ connected to it by the relation *

$$\omega = -g\eta\mathbf{H}. \tag{27}$$

In the classical case $g = 1$, there is an obvious relationship between formula (27) and Larmor's theorem: in fact, formula (27) means in this case that the magnetic effect of the rotation ω can be *compensated* by that of the magnetic field $-\mathbf{H}$ connected with ω by Larmor's relation $\omega = \eta \cdot (-\mathbf{H})$; and this statement is equivalent to Larmor's theorem. By measuring the magnetic field $-\mathbf{H}$ just sufficient to compensate the effect of the rotation ω, one obtains a determination of the factor $g\eta$. Using ferromagnetic substances, Barnett found a value of this quantity corresponding to a negative sign of the charge and a gyromagnetic ratio nearly equal to 2. The interpretation of this result is that *ferromagnetism is mainly due to the spins of the electrons*, with only a small resultant contribution from their translatory motions.

Einstein and de Haas observed the rotation set up when the magnetization of a thin iron cylinder was reversed and calculated the corresponding change $\delta\mathbf{G}$ of angular momentum. In virtue of the law of conservation of angular momentum, this change $\delta\mathbf{G}$ serves to compensate the angular momentum $\delta\mathbf{G}_m$ connected with the change of magnetization $\delta\mathbf{M}$ by the relation $\delta\mathbf{M} = -g\eta\,\delta\mathbf{G}_m$ similar to (26). We have therefore the relation

$$\delta\mathbf{M} = +g\,\eta\,\delta\mathbf{G}$$

between the observed quantities $\delta\mathbf{M}$ and $\delta\mathbf{G}$. This yields at once the sign and magnitude of the factor $g\eta$. The result of the experiment was in complete agreement with that of Barnett.

Subsequently the measurement of the Einstein – de Haas effect was extended by Sucksmith (1930) to paramagnetic substances,

---

* The identification (27) disregards the fact that μ and $\mathbf{J}$ contain terms depending on ω. The neglect of second-order effects in ω is justified, however, by the smallness of this quantity compared with atomic frequencies.

with a view to determining the corresponding Landé factors. The method yields values in good agreement with the spectroscopic determinations.

Another interesting application of the Einstein – de Haas effect is the determination of the gyromagnetic ratio of a substance in the *superconducting state*. As is well known, this state is characterized by the vanishing of the magnetic induction, i.e. by a strong diamagnetism (Meissner effect). It was found that the gyromagnetic ratio has in this case the classical value 1. This result suggests an interpretation of the diamagnetism arising in the superconducting state entirely in terms of the translatory motions of the electrons *.

7. MAXWELL'S CONSIDERATIONS CONCERNING THE INERTIA OF ELECTRIC CURRENTS

The way in which the gyromagnetic effects depend on the inertia of the motion of electricity is quite foreign to usual electrodynamics, in which the only inertia effects considered are those depending on mutual or self-induction. In his attempt to set up a comprehensive "dynamical theory of electromagnetism", Maxwell, however, gave very careful consideration to the possible existence of such gyromagnetic effects; the lack of positive experimental evidence led him to the right conclusion that they are in general negligibly small compared with the ordinary induction effects **. Maxwell observes that the total kinetic energy of a system of conductors and electric currents can be decomposed into three parts:

$$T = T_m + T_e + T_{em},$$

of which the first is the usual mechanical term, the second represents the magnetic energy of the system of currents, and the third is a function of both mechanical velocities and current intensities. Let Q_i, $\dot{Q}_i$ be the generalized co-ordinates and velocities of the

---

* I. Kikoin and S. Gubar, *Journ. Phys. U.S.S.R.*, **3**, 333, 1940.
** J. C. Maxwell, *Treatise on Electricity and Magnetism* (Oxford, 1873), vol. 2, chapt. VI.

material bodies; q_i, $\dot{q}_i$ those of the ions transporting the currents: T_m is a homogeneous quadratic function of the $\dot{Q}_i$ only, T_e a similar function of the $\dot{q}_i$ only, while T_{em} is bilinear in the $\dot{Q}_i$ and $\dot{q}_i$:

$$T_{em} = \sum_{i,k} C_{ik} \, \dot{Q}_i \dot{q}_k \, .$$

The functions T_m, T_e and T_{em} may depend on the Q_i in an arbitrary way, but it is natural to assume that they do not contain the q_i, i.e. that the latter are regarded as "cyclic" co-ordinates.

The terms T_e and T_{em} contribute to the dynamical equations describing the motion of the material bodies generalized force components given by

$$\frac{\partial T_e}{\partial Q_i} \quad \text{and} \quad -\frac{d}{dt}\left(\frac{\partial T_{em}}{\partial \dot{Q}_i}\right) + \frac{\partial T_{em}}{\partial Q_i}$$

respectively. The first force component, quadratic in the current intensities, represents the ordinary electrodynamic interaction between conductors traversed by currents. The second force component, however, is of the type which includes gyromagnetic effects. In fact, if Q_i is an angular co-ordinate, so that the mechanical term in the equation gives the rate of change of the corresponding component of angular momentum, the term

$$-\frac{d}{dt}\left(\frac{\partial T_{em}}{\partial \dot{Q}_i}\right) = -\frac{d}{dt}\left(\sum_k C_{ik} \, \dot{q}_k\right)$$

is proportional to the rate of change of the same component of the magnetic moment of the system of currents, and thus gives rise to the Einstein – de Haas effect. The term $\partial T_{em}/\partial Q_i$, on the other hand, leads to a kind of gyroscopic effect for a conductor in which a current is flowing and which rotates around an axis different from that of the current: owing to the inertia of the carriers of the current, there will be a tendency of the two axes towards parallelism, and the term in question is just the couple determining this phenomenon. Maxwell himself vainly attempted in 1861 to produce the effect, and it would even now be difficult to observe it.

The mixed term T_{em} will also give a contribution to the electro-magnetic equations

$$\frac{d}{dt}\left(\frac{\partial T_e}{\partial \dot{q}_i}\right) = -\left(\frac{T_{em}}{\partial \dot{q}_i}\right),$$

which expresses the law of induction for moving conductors. The right-hand side represents, for example, an electromotive force produced by imparting to a conductor either a rotation, as in the Barnett effect, or a linear acceleration, as has been done by Tolman in 1916. In the latter experiment the acceleration $\dot{v}$ gives rise to the electromotive force $(m/e)\dot{v}$ and the value obtained for e/m is the same as for cathode rays: it is thus shown in a direct way that metallic conduction is effected by electrons.

CHAPTER IV

MAGNETIC PROPERTIES OF MATTER

Our aim in this chapter will be to interpret the magnetic properties of matter, especially the three distinct types of magnetization — diamagnetism, paramagnetism, and ferromagnetism — in terms of the behaviour of the atoms in an external magnetic field. For the sake of simplicity we shall confine the discussion to a purely classical model of the atom, i.e. we shall take account only of the magnetism due to the orbital motions of the atomic electrons. When dealing with ferromagnetism we shall add a few words about the other extreme case of a magnetization entirely due to the spins of electrons; but we shall not enter into the complicated problems raised by the general case *.

1. INTRINSIC AND INDUCED MAGNETIC MOMENT; DIAMAGNETISM

It may happen that an atom or ion in its normal state has a net angular momentum $\mathbf{g}$, and consequently an *intrinsic* magnetic moment μ proportional to it, according to the relation (III, 21)

$$\mu = - \eta\mathbf{g}. \tag{1}$$

In general, all those individual atomic moments will be oriented at random and will not give rise to any average density of magnetization. If the body is placed in an external field, each atomic moment will perform a Larmor precession around the direction of the field: this in itself would make no change for the resultant magnetization, but on account of the exchange of energy between the atoms, governed by the laws of statistical mechanics, there will be a bias in favour of smaller values of the angle between the atomic moment and the direction of the field, and an average

---

* For further study, L. Bates' excellent book, *Modern Magnetism* (Cambridge, 1948), may be recommended.

component of magnetization in this direction will result: the substance will show a *paramagnetic* behaviour. We shall return presently to the detailed calculation of paramagnetism and to the explanation of the ferromagnetic phenomena related to it; we must now turn our attention to another general effect of the external field.

The Larmor precession gives rise to an additional angular momentum of the atom, which may be written $I \omega_L$, if I denotes the moment of inertia with respect to the axis through the nucleus O parallel to ω_L, viz. $I = \sum_k m_k s_k^2$. By formula (1), the field therefore *induces* a magnetic moment

$$\mu_d = -\eta \, I \, \omega_L = -\eta^2 \, I \, \mathbf{H},$$

in virtue of the definition (III, 15) of the Larmor frequency. This induced moment is always opposite to the field (whatever the sign of the charges producing it): it therefore gives rise to *diamagnetism*. If N denotes the number of atoms per unit volume, the average density of diamagnetic moment is

$$\mathbf{M}_d = -N \, \eta^2 \, \overline{I} \, \mathbf{H};$$

the bar over I indicates an average over all those orientations of the atoms with respect to the field that occur. If the atoms are oriented at random, or if (for any orientation) the electron distribution in the atom is spherically symmetrical, one has $\overline{s_k^2} = \frac{2}{3} \overline{r_k^2}$, where r_k is the distance of the kth electron from the nucleus O. Therefore $\overline{I} = \frac{2}{3} m \sum_k \overline{r_k^2}$, and we get for the diamagnetic moment density

$$\mathbf{M}_d = -\chi_d \, \mathbf{H}, \tag{2}$$

with the expression

$$\chi_d = \frac{1}{6} \cdot \frac{N e^2}{m \, c^2} \cdot \sum_k \overline{r_k^2} \tag{3}$$

for the *diamagnetic susceptibility*.

Diamagnetism, according to this view, is a general property of all substances. It exists whether or not there is any intrinsic magnetic moment and resulting paramagnetism. When the latter effect occurs, however, it is generally so much larger than the accompanying diamagnetism that it completely masks the diamagnetic contribution. Thus, only those substances which have no intrinsic magnetic moment exhibit the diamagnetic behaviour. Referred to one gram-atom, i.e. to L atoms, the diamagnetic susceptibility may be written, by inserting the numerical values given in Chapter I, Section 4:

$$\chi_d = 2.8 \cdot 10^{10} \cdot \sum_k \overline{r_k^2} \quad \text{c.g.s. units per gram-atom;}$$

taking for the atomic linear dimensions the estimate $a \approx 10^{-8}$ cm, we get for χ_d the order of magnitude 10^{-6} per gram-atom, which agrees with the measurements.

2. THE PARADOX OF THE CLASSICAL THEORY OF MAGNETISM

The result of the preceding analysis, according to which the external magnetic field produces a net diamagnetic effect, superposed in some cases upon a paramagnetic contribution from intrinsic magnetic moments of the atoms, seems very satisfactory. From the point of view of classical theory, however, it is entirely fallacious. We have already observed that in order to understand how the paramagnetic moment comes about it is essential to take the interactions between the atoms into consideration. In treating the diamagnetic effect, however, we have wrongly neglected these interactions. In fact, the correct procedure is to calculate quite generally the statistical average of the magnetic moment for an assembly of atoms in thermal equilibrium. If we apply this method we arrive at the paradoxical result that the average magnetic moment always vanishes: it is impossible to explain the magnetic properties of matter by a classical theory.

The argument is essentially that the magnetic moment is a function of the *velocities* (and not of the momenta) of the atomic electrons, and that if we express the Boltzmann distribution function in terms of the velocities it keeps exactly the same form as in the absence of any magnetic field. In fact, it has been shown in Chapter III, Section 2, that the Hamiltonian of a particle in the presence of a magnetic field, represented by its vector potential, is exactly the same function of the *velocity* of the particle as without field. Moreover, when we transform the element of volume in momentum space into the element of volume in velocity space, we see that the Jacobian determinant occurring as a factor in this transformation again reduces to a function of the velocities entirely independent of the vector potential. The statistical average of any quantity depending only on the velocities is thus independent of any magnetic field which may be present. The average magnetic moment must therefore vanish. This conclusion was reached independently, in 1911, by Niels Bohr and by Miss van Leeuwen in their doctoral dissertations.

In the simple case in which the atoms have no intrinsic moment in their normal state we may picture the cancellation of the diamagnetism as due to an opposing moment arising from a modification of the orbits of the electrons in the atoms as a result of their mutual interactions. This suggests the clue to the solution of the paradox. One of the fundamental postulates of quantum theory, by introducing the concept of *stationary state*, has the effect of ensuring a sufficient *stability* of the electronic orbits to prevent, in particular, the cancellation of magnetism by atomic interactions. Strictly speaking, only a quantal theory of magnetism can therefore be developed consistently. For the purpose of deriving the principal features of the phenomena, however, it is possible to pursue the classical line of approach, provided the (admittedly rough) assumption is made that the intrinsic magnetic moment of an atom is an invariable quantity, i.e. remains always the same for all atoms of the substance considered. By this assumption we smuggle (so to speak) an essential quantal feature into the theory, and we may perhaps with a better conscience proceed to the calculation of the paramagnetic moment as a statistical average.

3. PARAMAGNETISM

Consider a body of absolute temperature T in a constant magnetic field $\mathbf{H}$, and suppose that the interactions between the atoms may be disregarded (as for instance may be done in the case of an ideal gas or a dilute solution) *. The Boltzmann distribution function for an atom then has the form

$$\exp(-\mathbf{H}/kT)\, d\omega_q\, d\omega_p,$$

where k is Boltzmann's constant, $d\omega_q$ and $d\omega_p$ the volume elements in configuration and momentum space, and $\mathbf{H}$ is the Hamiltonian discussed in Chapter III, Section 3. It reduces for a constant magnetic field to the sum

$$\mathbf{H} = K_0 + K_m + K_m^{(2)}$$

of the kinetic energy K_0 in the absence of field and the two magnetic energy terms defined by (III, 12) and (III, 14). If we assume the intrinsic magnetic moment of the atom to be a constant vector μ, and call θ the angle between the vectors μ and $\mathbf{H}$, we may write the term $-K_m/kT$ as a function of θ only:

$$+ \alpha \cos\theta, \quad \text{with} \quad \alpha = \mu H/kT.$$

The second order term $K_m^{(2)}$ will further be neglected.

The density of magnetization M_p in the direction of the field is given by N times the average of the component $\mu \cos\theta$ of the atomic moment. Of all the degrees of freedom of the atom we have thus to retain only those pertaining to its rotation around its centre of mass O: they are characterized by the Eulerian angles θ, φ, ψ (defined with respect to the direction of the field) and the conjugate momenta p_θ, p_φ, p_ψ. The corresponding contribution from the kinetic energy K_0,

$$K_0' = \frac{1}{2A}\left\{ p_\theta^2 + \frac{1}{\sin^2\theta}\,(p_\varphi - p_\psi \cos\theta)^2 \right\} + \frac{1}{2C}\, p_\psi^2,$$

is in fact the only one containing the variable θ in which we are interested; C and A are the moments of inertia of the atom around the direction of μ, assumed to be an axis of symmetry, and any direction perpendicular to it.

---

* It should be remembered that, although the interactions between the atoms may have no quantitative effect on the statistical distribution, the *existence* of such interactions is quite essential for the establishment of the thermal equilibrium.

We have therefore to evaluate the quantity

$$M_p = M_s \cdot \frac{\int \cos \theta \cdot \exp \{a \cos \theta - (K_0'/kT)\} \, d\omega}{\int \exp \{a \cos \theta - (K_0'/kT)\} \, d\omega},$$

with $M_s = N\mu$ and $d\omega = d\theta \, d\varphi \, d\psi \, dp_\theta \, dp_\varphi \, dp_\psi$. Clearly, the integrations over φ, ψ and p_θ give the same constant factor in the two terms of the fraction and may be disregarded. The double integration over p_φ and p_ψ also gives the same factor in the two terms, but this factor is proportional to $\sin \theta$ (as may readily be seen, without carrying out the integrations, by a suitable transformation of variables) *. There remains, therefore, an integration in both terms over $\sin \theta \, d\theta$, i.e. we have

$$M_p = M_s \cdot \frac{\int_{-1}^{+1} u \, du \exp (a u)}{\int_{-1}^{+1} du \exp (a u)},$$

or finally

$$M_p = M_s \left(\coth a - \frac{1}{a} \right)$$

with $M_s = N\mu,$ $a = \mu H / kT.$ (4)

This formula was derived by Langevin in 1905; the function

$$L(a) = \coth a - \frac{1}{a}$$

is called the *Langevin function*. It is represented in Figure 1, which exhibits the main qualitative features of paramagnetism. The fact that the magnetization depends on the argument $a = \mu H / kT$ illustrates the opposite influences of thermal agitation and of the external field: increasing thermal agitation and decreasing energy of Larmor precession have the same tendency: to bring about a more and more isotropic distribution of the atomic

---

* Usually, this factor $\sin \theta$ is simply introduced as part of an element of solid angle $\sin \theta \, d\theta \, d\varphi$, while the integrations over momentum variables and the kinetic energy contribution to the Boltzmann factor are ignored. Although this short-cut looks plausible enough, its rigorous justification requires the argument just developed.

moments, with a resulting decrease of the average magnetization. For small fields and high temperatures (which includes the most

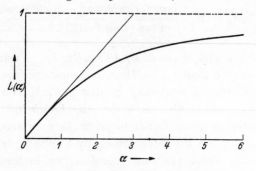

Fig. 1. The Langevin function

usual conditions of observation) we have $L(a) \approx \frac{1}{3} a$, and the magnetization is approximately proportional to the field:

$$M_p \approx \chi_p H \qquad [a \text{ small}]. \tag{5}$$

This defines the *paramagnetic susceptibility*

$$\chi_p = \frac{1}{3} \cdot \frac{N \mu^2}{kT} . \tag{6}$$

The opposite extreme of large fields or low temperatures leads asymptotically to a state of *saturation*

$$M_p \approx M_s \qquad [a \text{ large}], \tag{7}$$

in which all atomic moments are oriented in the direction of the field.

Langevin's theory of paramagnetism conforms with the experiment. At first sight it would seem to be applicable only to paramagnetic substances in the gaseous state, such as oxygen. But the structure of the typical paramagnetic salts explains how a theory in which the magnetic atoms or ions are treated as independent can account for the behaviour of these substances even in the solid state. In fact, the intrinsic magnetic moments in the paramagnetic salts belong to ions of either the iron group or the group of rare earths; they are due to the contribution from an incomplete inner electronic shell (the 3d and the 4f shell respectively) which is more or less effectively shielded by the outer electrons against external perturbations. The magnetic properties of these salts have been extensively studied down to temperatures of small fractions of one degree absolute; in particular, the phenomenon of saturation predicted by the theory has been observed. The susceptibility, when referred to a fixed number of atoms, such as a gram-atom, varies, according to (6), inversely as the absolute temperature; this behaviour, which contrasts so markedly with that of the temperature-independent diamagnetic susceptibility, was discovered by Curie (1895). Curie's law has been found to hold down to temperatures of the order of a degree absolute.

The order of magnitude of the paramagnetic saturation moments M_s and susceptibilities χ_p can be estimated by observing that in quantum theory components of angular momentum appear as integral multiples of the fundamental quantity $h/2\pi$, where h denotes Planck's constant. Therefore the unit of intrinsic magnetic moment is, by formula (1), the *magneton*

$$\mu_0 = -\eta \cdot \frac{h}{2\pi} = 9.27 \cdot 10^{-21} \quad \text{erg} \cdot \text{gauss}^{-1}. \tag{8}$$

The corresponding saturation moment per gram-atom is

$$L\mu_0 = 5580 \text{ erg} \cdot \text{gauss}^{-1} \cdot (\text{gram-atom})^{-1},$$

and the susceptibility per gram-atom

$$\frac{1}{3} \cdot \frac{L\mu_0^2}{kT} = \frac{0.125}{T} \quad \text{c.g.s. units/gram-atom},$$

which gives, for $T \approx 300°$ K, values of the order of 10^{-4}, i.e. about 100 times larger than the diamagnetic susceptibilities.

For a more quantitative study the methods of quantum mechanics are indispensable. On account of its application to ferromagnetism we shall mention the simple case in which the intrinsic moment is due to the spin of a single free electron. There are then only two possible orientations in the external field, either parallel or antiparallel, yielding the contributions $\pm \mu$ with the relative Boltzmann factors $\exp(\pm a)$ to M_p. Therefore

$$M_p = M_s \cdot \frac{\exp a - \exp(-a)}{\exp a + \exp(-a)} = M_s \cdot \tanh a. \qquad (9)$$

The Langevin function is replaced by a hyperbolic tangent, which has the same general behaviour. The expression for the susceptibility, however, is 3 times larger than the classical expression (6). Since the spin angular momentum is $\frac{1}{2} \cdot h/2\pi$, while its relation to the intrinsic magnetic moment is given by (III, 22), we have in this case $\mu = \mu_0$.

4. FERROMAGNETISM

In the preceding theory of paramagnetism the interactions of the atoms have been completely neglected. The average effect of these interactions (whether or not of magnetic origin) on any atom may be represented, at any rate for the sake of a preliminary investigation, by an equivalent *internal magnetic field*, whose action must be added to that of the external field. Now, if this internal field happens to be very large, it will give rise to a magnetization approaching saturation for a quite small, or even vanishing, value of the external field: the occurrence of such a large "spontaneous magnetization", however, is an important characteristic of ferromagnetism, especially conspicuous for single crystals of the ferromagnetic metals. The idea of explaining ferromagnetism by the presence of a large internal field is due to Weiss (1907), who developed it on a phenomenological basis without enquiring into the nature of the internal field.

Weiss' theory is based on the assumption that the internal field $\mathbf{H}_i$ is proportional to the magnetization:

$$\mathbf{H}_i = W\mathbf{M}. \qquad (10)$$

In the expression (4) or (9) for the magnetization in terms of field and temperature, the external field $\mathbf{H}$ must be replaced by $\mathbf{H} + \mathbf{H}_i$. Weiss himself worked with Langevin's formula (4); we shall take the more adequate formula (9), with $\mu = \mu_0$. The relation between

the magnetization and the external field is then given, according
to (9)· and (10), in the implicit form

$$M = M_s \cdot \tanh a$$

$$a = \frac{\mu_0}{kT}(H + WM) ,$$

or

$$\frac{M}{M_s} = \tanh a$$

$$\frac{M}{M_s} = \frac{T}{\Theta} a - \frac{H}{WM_s} , \qquad (11)$$

with Θ defined by

$$k\, \Theta = \mu_0 \, WM_s. \qquad (12)$$

The discussion of the system (11) is carried out most conveniently
by a graphical method. In Figure 2 the ratio M/M_s is plotted
against a as it is given by each equation of the system (11). The

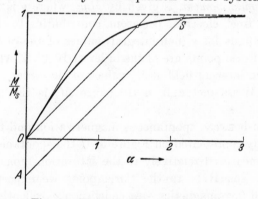

Fig. 2.   Theory of ferromagnetism

first equation represents the usual paramagnetic curve, the second
yields, for various values of the external field H, a group of parallel
straight lines, the slope of which is T/Θ. Thus the temperature
fixes the slope of the straight lines; the value of the external field
then determines a point A on the M/M_s-axis at a distance $-H/WM_s$
from the origin. The straight line through A intersects the paramagnetic curve at a point S which indicates the value of M/M_s
corresponding to the given values of H and T.

Let us consider in particular the case $H = 0$, i.e. the straight line through the origin. It depends on the temperature whether or not this line intersects the paramagnetic curve at a point S other than the origin itself. Since the slope of the tangent to the curve at the origin is unity, there is such a point S provided that T is smaller than the critical temperature Θ defined by (12); this corresponds to a *spontaneous magnetization*, which increases asymptotically towards the value M_s as the temperature decreases. Above the temperature Θ, however, the substance presents a normal paramagnetic behaviour. This remarkable property of ferromagnetic substances was also discovered by Curie; the critical temperature Θ is called the *Curie point* of the substance. For the ferromagnetic metals the saturation values of the magnetization are of the expected order of magnitude of about 10^4 erg · gauss^{-1} · · (gram-atom)$^{-1}$. More precisely, the saturation moment per gram-atom, or *atomic moment*, is given by $\nu L \mu_0$, where ν is the average number of "free" electrons per atom, contributing to the magnetization; one finds for ν (non-integral) values of the order of a few units. The Curie points are of the order of $1000°$ K, which by (12) gives for the internal field WM_s values of the order of 10^7 gauss, or for the Weiss factor $W \approx 10^4$ (since M_s is the moment per unit *volume*).

The relation between spontaneous magnetization and temperature is graphically represented on Figure 3. If the spontaneous magnetization is measured relatively to the saturation moment and the temperature relatively to the Curie point we expect the same curve for all ferromagnetics — a conclusion excellently borne out by the experimental data. This universal curve depends only on the function of α assumed as the law of paramagnetism; the data fit the tanh α-law quite well and rule out the Langevin function: this confirms the view that here the magnetization is mainly due to the electron spins.

Above the Curie point we may replace in (11) tanh α by α and obtain a proportionality law $M_p = \chi_p H$, with a susceptibility

$$\chi_p = \frac{\Theta}{W} \cdot \frac{1}{T - \Theta} \cdot \qquad (13)$$

This *Curie–Weiss law* resembles the ordinary Curie law for para-
magnetics, except that temperatures must be counted from the
Curie point and not from the absolute zero. As a matter of fact,

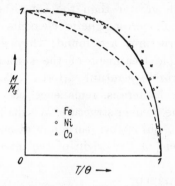

Fig. 3. Spontaneous magnetization. The full curve corresponds to the
tanh a-law, the dotted curve to the $L(a)$-law

since there is always some internal field, Curie's law would appear
as an approximation to the more accurate relation (13).

At ordinary temperatures the spontaneous magnetization is very
near to the saturation value and the application of an external
field has not much further effect. In other words, we should expect
a body obeying the magnetization law (11), with a high value of
the internal field, to remain permanently magnetized to saturation.
In practice this ideal behaviour is not directly observed, although
it is approximated by very pure single crystals of the ferromagnetic
elements. The actual behaviour of ferromagnetics, which consist
of aggregates of microscopic crystals of various orientations, is
determined by the existence of juxtaposed small regions, the so-
called *Weiss domains*, magnetized to saturation according to the
ideal law just discussed, but with magnetic moments oriented at
random. The effect of an external magnetic field is to shift the
boundaries of these domains, with a general tendency to favour
orientation parallel to itself. At first only small reversible shifts
are produced, but for larger values of the external field irreversible
processes occur, involving boundary shifts which sweep over a
whole domain: the accompanying pulses of current induced in a

coil can be made audible in a telephone, and the closer study of this *Barkhausen effect* gives information about the average size of the Weiss domains; they are found to contain about 10^{15} atoms, and are thus much greater than the constituent microcrystals. In single crystals of ferromagnetic elements very simple and regular domain structures are found; they are made directly visible by a suitable treatment of the surface of the crystal, whereby they give rise to beautiful patterns *. The familiar features of ferromagnetism: hysteresis, remanence, coercitivity, find their interpretation in the domain structure. We shall not discuss those questions, however, but rather turn our attention to the more fundamental problem of the origin of the internal field.

5. THE INTERNAL FIELD

Let us begin with the examination of the obvious contribution to the internal field which arises from the *magnetic interactions* of the atoms or ions carrying intrinsic moments. The evaluation of this field is conveniently performed by a method due to Lorentz. Let us select an atom at random and imagine a physically infinitesimal sphere having its centre at this atom. This sphere divides the surrounding atoms into two groups, those outside and those inside the sphere, whose respective contributions $\mathbf{H}_1$ and $\mathbf{H}_2$ to the field at the centre of the sphere will now be discussed separately.

The evaluation of the field $\mathbf{H}_1$ can be carried out in a perfectly general way. We may imagine the matter inside the sphere removed from the body, while the atoms in the rest of the body are maintained in the situation they occupied before the removal of the small sphere. The problem is then to find the magnetic field produced in a hollow spherical cavity inside a body of uniform magnetization $\mathbf{M}$. In formal analogy to the corresponding electrical problem, we may regard this field as due to a distribution of "free magnetic poles" on the surface of the cavity with a density $\mathbf{M} \cdot \mathbf{n}$

---

* See, for example, H. Williams, R. Bozorth and W. Shockley, *Phys. Rev.*, **75**, 155, 1949; H. Williams and W. Shockley, *ibid.*, **75**, 178, 1949.

(the unit vector **n** pointing towards the centre of the cavity). Now, it is quite easy to show that this field is uniform throughout the whole cavity and equal to $\frac{1}{3}$ **M**. We may consider the surface distribution of poles as resulting from a passage to the limit from the superposition of two equal magnetic spheres of uniform pole density ϱ, the one positive, the other negative, displaced with respect to each other in the direction of **M** by an amount **d**, such that $\varrho\mathbf{d} = \mathbf{M}$; when so defined, the vector **d** points from the centre of the positive sphere O_+ to that of the negative sphere O_-. Let $\mathbf{r}_+$, $\mathbf{r}_-$ be the radii vectores from O_+ and O_- to any point P inside the cavity, so that $\mathbf{d} = \mathbf{r}_+ - \mathbf{r}_-$. The field at P due to the positive sphere has the direction of $\mathbf{r}_+$ and its magnitude H_+ is obtained, e.g., by applying Gauss' theorem to the sphere of centre O_+ passing through P:

$$H_+ \cdot 4\pi r_+^2 = \varrho \cdot \frac{4\pi}{3} r_+^3 \; ;$$

hence $\mathbf{H}_+ = \frac{1}{3} \varrho\, \mathbf{r}_+$. Similarly, $\mathbf{H}_- = -\frac{1}{3} \varrho\, \mathbf{r}_-$, and the total field at P is $\mathbf{H}_+ + \mathbf{H}_- = \frac{1}{3} \varrho\, (\mathbf{r}_+ - \mathbf{r}_-) = \frac{1}{3} \varrho\, \mathbf{d}$. The contribution of the atoms outside the sphere to the internal field is thus quite generally

$$\mathbf{H}_1 = \tfrac{1}{3}\,\mathbf{M}. \tag{14}$$

For the contribution $\mathbf{H}_2$ of the atoms inside the sphere no universal expression can be given. Lorentz could only show that it vanishes if the atoms form a cubic lattice; but in general it will be expected to give some average contribution proportional to **M**, like $\mathbf{H}_1$, and presumably of the same order of magnitude or smaller.

The internal field of magnetic origin thus appears to be of the form assumed by Weiss: in fact, it was Lorentz' formula (14) which actually suggested to Weiss the form of his assumption (10). Quantitatively, however, it is quite inadequate to account for the order of magnitude of the fields needed for an explanation of ferromagnetism: the Weiss field must clearly have another origin. The riddle could only be solved after the advent of quantum mechanics in 1928, when Heisenberg pointed out the occurrence of short-range interatomic forces, the so-called *exchange inter-*

actions, as a consequence of the exclusion principle which the interacting electron systems must satisfy. No classical picture can be given of these typically quantal forces. We shall only mention here that they can be shown to give rise, in our case, to an action on a magnetized atom or ion equivalent to that of a magnetic field of the Weiss type. In general, however, the proportionality factor W will be negative, and sufficiently large positive values of W, as required for ferromagnetism, can only be expected for a rather narrow range of values of the ratio between the distance of neighbouring atoms in the crystal lattice and the radius of the incomplete electron shell in the atom.

Many paramagnetic substances obey a Curie–Weiss law either with small positive or with negative values of Θ. According to what has just been stated, this property can be understood in a general way in terms of an internal field, although the detailed analysis of most cases involves additional complications. An interesting example is iron alum, whose behaviour at very low temperatures closely resembles ferromagnetism, with a Curie point at $\Theta = 0.03°$ K, corresponding to an internal field of the order of the Lorentz field (14).

CHAPTER V

ELECTRIC POLARIZATION AND OPTICAL DISPERSION

The theory of electric polarization can be developed in close
analogy to that of magnetization, and there are examples of
electrical phenomena presenting a more or less complete analogy
to the three types of magnetism discussed in the preceding chapter.
When we pass, however, from the consideration of the effects of
constant external fields on matter to that of the rapidly variable
electromagnetic field of light waves, the electric phenomena
become predominant, whereas the magneto-optical effects (such
as the Zeeman effect) appear as relatively small perturbations.
The reason for this difference is that the respective forces exerted
by the magnetic and the electric field of a light wave on an atomic
electron have the same small ratio to each other as the velocity
of the electron to the velocity of light: this is immediately apparent
from our expression for the Lorentz force when it is remembered
that, in our system of units, the amplitudes of these fields are
exactly or nearly the same. In the present chapter we shall first
give a brief outline of the theory of electric polarization for constant fields, and thereafter present an extension of these considerations to periodic fields, which leads to an elementary theory
of optical dispersion and related phenomena.

1. ELECTRIC POLARIZATION IN CONSTANT FIELDS

For a general molecular system composed of a certain number of
particles of charges e_k and masses m_k the electric dipole moment is
defined by

$$\mathbf{p} = \sum_k e_k \mathbf{x}_k; \tag{1}$$

since the total charge vanishes, the origin of the vectors $\mathbf{x}_k$ is
arbitrary. As in the magnetic case, we may distinguish an intrinsic
and an induced dipole moment. The former is present in the normal

state of the molecule even in the absence of an external field; we shall assume that it has a constant value, not perturbed by the molecular interactions. The induced moment will always arise on application of an external field, independently of the presence of any intrinsic moment, as a result of the distortion of the molecule by the forces pulling the positive and the negative charges in opposite directions.

The amplitude of this distortion is readily derived, for each particle, from the equilibrium condition between the external force $e_k\mathbf{E}$ and the quasi-elastic force $\mathbf{F}_k = -m_k\omega_k^2(\mathbf{x}_k - \mathbf{d}_k)$ which holds the particle at its equilibrium position of co-ordinates $\mathbf{d}_k$. In this notation ω_k is the circular frequency of the proper oscillation of the particle around its equilibrium position and $\mathbf{p}_a = \sum e_k\mathbf{d}_k$ is the intrinsic dipole moment. The condition just mentioned may be written

$$\mathbf{x}_k - \mathbf{d}_k = \frac{e_k}{m_k\omega_k^2}\,\mathbf{E},$$

whence we get for the *induced* dipole moment

$$\mathbf{p} = \sum_k e_k(\mathbf{x}_k - \mathbf{d}_k) = \gamma_a\,\mathbf{E}, \tag{2}$$

with the *molecular coefficient of polarizability*

$$\gamma_a = \sum_k \frac{e_k^2}{m_k\omega_k^2}. \tag{3}$$

The induced electric polarization per unit volume $\mathbf{P}$ is obtained by multiplying $\mathbf{p}$ by the number N of molecules per unit volume:

$$\mathbf{P} = \gamma_e\mathbf{E}, \quad \text{with} \quad \gamma_e = N\gamma_a; \tag{4}$$

γ_e is the polarizability per unit volume.

At this stage it must be emphasized that equation (2) embodies a considerable restriction on the type of molecules to which the preceding theory of induced polarization applies. In fact, in this equation we have only considered the polarizing action of the external field and disregarded the circumstance that, when a dipole moment is induced in the constituent atoms of a molecule, the interior field due to their dipole interactions must be added to the external field to determine the final value of the total dipole moment induced in the molecule *. Now, this interior field will in general exhibit an anisotropy, determined by the structure of the molecule; consequently, the relation between induced dipole moment and external field, while still linear, will not reduce to a simple proportionality but will involve a *tensor of polarizability*. The validity of the theory based on the formulae (2) and (3) is therefore essentially limited to atoms and to those molecules whose interior dipole field is sufficiently weak.

The coefficient of induced polarizability is essentially determined by the structure of the molecules, and when referred to a gram-atom (rather than to the unit volume) it is independent of the temperature. In order to explain the façt that the dielectric constants of certain substances, in contrast to this property, show a marked variation with temperature, Debye (1912), guided by the magnetic analogy, pointed out that this behaviour could be due to the existence of intrinsic dipole moments. In fact, such a moment, under the action of the couple exerted on it by the external field, will perform oscillations in a plane, and the potential energy of this motion, given by (III, 9), is of the same form as the kinetic energy of the Larmor precession in the corresponding magnetic case. The statistical treatment of paramagnetism can therefore be transposed immediately to the case of electric dipoles, in spite of the characteristic difference between the "gyroscopic" behaviour of a magnetic atom and the "pendular" motion of an electric dipole. The contribution of the intrinsic dipoles to the polarization is given by a formula similar to Langevin's:

$$P_d = P_s L(a), \quad \text{with} \quad a = \frac{p_a E}{kT}, \tag{5}$$

where $P_s = N p_a$ represents a saturation value. Usually one observes an approximately linear dependence on the field:

$$P_d = \gamma_d E, \tag{6}$$

---

* The *interior* field considered here should not be confused with the *internal* field introduced later in this section; the former is due to the interactions between the atoms in a single molecule, the latter to the interaction between the different molecules.

with a polarizability

$$\gamma_d = \frac{1}{3} \cdot \frac{N p_a^2}{kT} \tag{7}$$

obeying a "Curie law" of inverse proportionality with temperature. The total polarizability

$$\gamma = \gamma_e + \gamma_d \tag{8}$$

is thus of the form $a + \beta/T$.

Debye's theory has been brilliantly confirmed by numerous measurements. From the empirical determination of the coefficient β of the law of temperature variation the intrinsic moment can be derived. This quantity is now known for a large number of compounds, mainly organic; the values obtained are of the order of magnitude of 10^{-18} electrostatic c.g.s units, as one would expect from molecular dimensions of the order $a \approx 10^{-8}$ cm. One important consequence of the knowledge of intrinsic dipole moments has been to confirm the actual geometrical significance of the structure formulae of chemistry: the numerical values found for the dipole moments can be understood from the spatial distribution of the constituent ions as described by the chemical structure formula. In particular, the existence of an intrinsic dipole moment implies an asymmetry in the structure of the molecule *.

The polarizability γ defines the relation of proportionality between the total polarization and the average field acting on the molecules to produce it. In the preceding argument we have provisionally identified this field with the external field $\mathbf{E}$. More accurately, it is necessary to add the action of the internal field, which, in dielectrics, is essentially determined by the electric dipole interactions of the molecules. The internal field is therefore given by a formula of the type

$$\mathbf{E}_i = (\tfrac{1}{3} + s)\,\mathbf{P}, \tag{9}$$

where the contribution $s\,\mathbf{P}$ is due to the molecules most closely surrounding the given one, while $\tfrac{1}{3}\mathbf{P}$ is the Lorentz field produced

---

* The various aspects and implications of this subject are authoritatively discussed by P. Debye, *Polar Molecules* (New York, 1929).

by the more distant molecules. From the relation

$$\mathbf{P} = \gamma(\mathbf{E} + \mathbf{E}_i)$$

combined with the expression (9) we derive the true law of proportionality between polarization and external field:

$$\mathbf{P} = \varkappa\mathbf{E}, \tag{10}$$

with the *dielectric susceptibility*

$$\varkappa = \gamma / \{1 - \gamma(\tfrac{1}{3} + s)\}. \tag{11}$$

The *dielectric constant* ε is then defined in the usual way by

$$\varepsilon = 1 + \varkappa. \tag{12}$$

On the assumption (usually fulfilled) that $s = 0$, the polarizability may be expressed, by (11) and (12), in terms of the dielectric constant as

$$\tfrac{1}{3}\gamma = \frac{\varepsilon-1}{\varepsilon+2}. \tag{13}$$

The interest of this formula will appear in the next section, when it will be transposed to the domain of optics.

The linear approximation (10) will do for most cases. But there are a few instances of dielectric crystals which show saturation at ordinary temperatures and in relatively weak fields. The most famous case is that of the so-called *Rochelle salt* or Seignette salt, a tartrate of formula $NaKC_4H_4O_6 \cdot 4H_2O$, prepared for the first time in 1672 by an apothecary of La Rochelle called Seignette. Rochelle salt has a Curie point at about 24° C, above which the polarizability follows a Curie–Weiss law. At temperatures below the Curie point * its behaviour under the action of an electric field is strikingly similar to that of a ferromagnetic; hysteresis phenomena reveal the existence of a domain structure **. The internal field may be represented by formula (9), with a value of $s \approx 0.16$; the intrinsic moment p_a is also of the normal order of magnitude of about 10^{-18} electrostatic units. Another group of "Seignette-

---

* There is another Curie point at −18° C, below which the crystal again behaves normally, the polarizability obeying a Curie–Weiss law. This lower Curie point is supposed to be connected with a temperature variation of the number of intrinsic dipole moments contributing to the polarization.
** See an article by A. von Hippel, *Rev. Mod. Phys.*, **22**, 221, 1950, in which the similar case of barium titanate $BaTiO_3$ is fully discussed and illustrated.

electrics" (of the type KH_2PO_4) was discovered by Busch and Scherrer in 1935; they have rather lower Curie points (of the order of $100°$ K).

2. ELEMENTARY THEORY OF DISPERSION

When a monochromatic light wave impinges upon an assembly of molecules, its main effect (neglecting magnetic actions) is to induce an electric polarization of the molecules, which varies periodically in time with the same frequency as the incident wave. All these vibrating dipoles in turn emit secondary waves, which interfere between them and with the incident wave and eventually give rise to the propagation through the medium (if it is isotropic) of a single resultant wave of the same frequency but of modified phase velocity: the ratio of the velocity of propagation of light *in vacuo* to its velocity in the medium is the *refractive index* of the medium. The variation of the refractive index with frequency constitutes the phenomenon of *dispersion*. In the course of its propagation through the medium, part of the energy carried by the wave is lost either by *scattering* out of the direction of propagation, or by true *absorption*, i.e. dissipation in the form of thermal motions of the molecules.

The rigorous analysis of this complicated mechanism requires rather delicate considerations. Before attempting it, it will be advisable to obtain a general orientation in the subject by taking, so to speak, a short cut based on an extrapolation to arbitrary frequencies of the fundamental result derived in Maxwell's electromagnetic theory for the limiting case of very low frequencies. For an isotropic, non-magnetic and non-conducting medium it is shown that the refractive index at low frequencies is related to the dielectric constant by the simple relation

$$n^2 = \varepsilon. \tag{14}$$

Combining this relation with (13), we find a relationship between the refractive index and a purely molecular property, the polarizability:

$$\tfrac{1}{3}\gamma = \frac{n^2-1}{n^2+2}. \tag{15}$$

Our elementary theory of dispersion consists in assuming the validity of the relation (15) for all frequencies. The problem is then reduced to the calculation of the polarizability as a function of the frequency of the incident wave — a comparatively simple affair. The phenomena of absorption and scattering, neglected at this stage, will be dealt with subsequently in a somewhat schematic way, which, however, suffices to bring out the main features. The formula (15) has been proposed almost at the same time by Lorentz, the great Dutchman to whom we owe the main ideas of the theory of electrons, and by a distinguished Danish physicist called Lorenz; "which (writes Lorentz) is certainly a curious case of coincidence". From this circumstance the formula derives its rather awkward name of *Lorentz–Lorenz relation*.

Before proceeding further, we may observe that relation (15), or rather a slight modification of it, can be put to practical use in the following way. If we refer the polarizability to a gram-molecule we may write

$$\tfrac{1}{3}\,\gamma_{\text{mol}} = \frac{\mu}{\delta} \cdot \frac{n^2 - 1}{n^2 + 2}, \tag{16}$$

where μ denotes the molecular weight and δ the mass density of the substance considered. Now, for a non-polar substance (i.e. if there is no intrinsic dipole moment), the polarizability per gram-molecule $\gamma_{\text{mol}} = L\gamma_a$ occurring on the left-hand side has a nearly additive character, in the sense that it is a sum of contributions from the single constituents of the molecule, and that these contributions may be regarded as approximately independent of each other: in fact, the proper frequencies ω_k will generally not be considerably modified by interactions with other molecules of the same or of a different kind. Consequently the refractive index (at any frequency) of a mixture or even of a chemical compound can be directly estimated, according to the schematic formula

$$\left(\frac{\mu}{\delta} \frac{n^2 - 1}{n^2 + 2} \right)_{\text{AB}} = \left(\frac{\mu}{\delta} \frac{n^2 - 1}{n^2 + 2} \right)_{\text{A}} + \left(\frac{\mu}{\delta} \frac{n^2 - 1}{n^2 + 2} \right)_{\text{B}},$$

from the knowledge of the refractive indices of the constituents at the same frequency.

Let us now work out the frequency dependence of the polarizability of molecules without intrinsic dipole moment. This frequency dependence arises from the inertia of the charged particles set in forced oscillation by the electric field of the incident light wave. Assuming the wave-length of the light large compared with atomic dimensions (which only excludes the domain of hard X-rays), we may treat the electric field of the wave as of constant amplitude over the whole system, and write the equation of motion of the kth particle in the form

$$\ddot{\mathbf{x}}_k + \omega_k^2\, \mathbf{x}_k = \frac{e_k}{m_k}\, \mathbf{e} \cdot \exp i\omega t. \qquad (17)$$

Consider a solution of the type

$$\mathbf{x}_k = \mathbf{x}_{k0} \exp i\omega t,$$

representing a forced oscillation of frequency ω. The amplitude $\mathbf{x}_{k0}$ is given by

$$\mathbf{x}_{k0} = \frac{e_k}{m_k} \cdot \frac{1}{\omega_k^2 - \omega^2} \cdot \mathbf{e}. \qquad (18)$$

This formula illustrates the reduction in the amplitude of the oscillation when the particle is forced to vibrate with a frequency different from that of its proper oscillation; the singularity occurring for $\omega = \omega_k$ merely indicates that the neglect of the damping of the oscillation ceases to be legitimate in this *resonance* region. We shall return to this point in the next section.

From (18) we derive for the amplitude $\mathbf{p} = \sum e_k \mathbf{x}_{k0}$ of the induced moment $\mathbf{p} \exp i\omega t$ an expression of the form

$$\mathbf{p} = \gamma_a\, \mathbf{e},$$

with

$$\gamma_a = \sum_k \frac{e_k^2}{m_k} \cdot \frac{1}{\omega_k^2 - \omega^2}\,; \qquad (19)$$

the last expression being an extension of that for the molecular polarizability (3), to which it reduces for $\omega = 0$. For the polarizability per unit volume γ we thus get the *dispersion formula*

$$\gamma = N \sum_k \frac{e_k^2}{m_k} \cdot \frac{1}{\omega_k^2 - \omega^2}. \qquad (20)$$

In the dispersion formula for atoms all terms are due to electrons and thus involve the same ratio e^2/m; the order of magnitude of the proper frequencies ranges from the visible to the far ultraviolet. In the case of molecules, however, there occur, besides such electronic terms, further contributions from the vibrations of the nuclei of the constituent atoms around their equilibrium positions and from the rotation of the molecule as a whole; these terms involve masses m_k of the order of the atomic masses. The corresponding vibration and rotation frequencies lie in the infra-red; in fact, they are to the electronic frequencies in the ratio of the square root of electronic to atomic mass, since the product $m_k\omega_k^2$ gives in each case the order of magnitude of the quasi-elastic binding force, which is of electrical origin and thus of the same order for electrons and nuclei.

The treatment of the problem by quantum mechanics leads to a formula of the same type; historically, in fact, the clue to a consistent formulation of quantum mechanics was given by Kramers' and Heisenberg's investigation of the problem of optical dispersion in the light of the correspondence principle. The proper frequencies of the classical oscillators correspond to the actual resonance frequencies determined by differences of energies of stationary states. In molecules this correspondence is very close between the classical and quantal frequencies of rotation and vibration of the constituent atoms. In atoms, however, and in molecules so far as electronic motions are concerned, the correspondence is of a less immediate character: each proper frequency can no more be associated with a single electron, but, in a certain sense, each electron contributes partially to the dispersion of any proper frequency. Accordingly each term of the quantal dispersion formula pertaining to electronic motion appears multiplied by a non-integral factor f_k, called the *strength* of the corresponding oscillator; for an atom with Z electrons one has, of course, $\sum f_k = Z$.

The variation of the polarizability with frequency is illustrated in Figure 4. For very high frequencies the polarizability remains negative and tends to zero; the refractive index accordingly is smaller than 1 and tends to unity. In so far as our formula may

still be used in this region, we may thus deduce from it, in virtue
of (15), the approximate relation

$$n^2 - 1 \approx -N_e \cdot \frac{e^2}{m} \cdot \frac{1}{\omega^2}; \qquad (21)$$

we have here neglected any contribution from atomic nuclei and
introduced the average number of electrons per unit volume N_e.

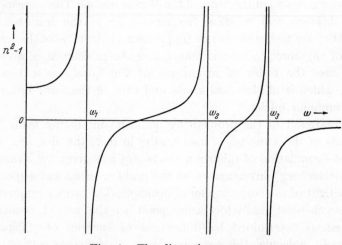

Fig. 4.   The dispersion curve

In this extreme case each electron independently contributes a
term $e^2/m\omega^2$ to the polarizability as if it moved freely in the medium:
in fact, the essential approximation made here consists in neglecting
the acceleration due to the binding force $\mathbf{F}_k$ in comparison with
the purely inertial effect induced by the electric force of the light
wave.

3. ANOMALOUS DISPERSION AND ABSORPTION

In the resonance regions around the proper frequencies ω_k the
dispersion formula must be corrected for the influence of the
damping of the oscillators. If we complete the fundamental
equation (17) by the introduction of a damping force proportional

to the velocity of the oscillating particle — $\dot{x}_k/B_k$, the corresponding term in the expression for the polarizability becomes

$$\gamma_k = N \frac{e_k^2}{m_k} \cdot \frac{1}{\omega_k^2 - \omega^2 + i\omega\Gamma_k}$$

$$= N \frac{e_k^2}{m_k} \cdot \frac{\omega_k^2 - \omega^2 - i\omega\Gamma_k}{(\omega_k^2 - \omega^2)^2 + \omega^2\Gamma_k^2} \tag{22}$$

with $$\Gamma_k = (m_k B_k)^{-1},$$

which gives rise to a complex refractive index.

Now, as is well known in optics, a complex refractive index means that the propagation of the wave in the medium is accompanied by absorption. In fact, if we put

$$n = n_0(1 - i\beta), \tag{23}$$

the spatial phase factor of the wave progressing in the medium in the direction of the Ox-axis (say) takes the form

$$\exp\left(-i\omega\frac{n}{c}x\right) = \exp\left(-i\omega\frac{n_0}{c}x\right) \cdot \exp\left(-\beta\omega\frac{n_0}{c}x\right);$$

this means that the intensity of the wave decreases as it progresses according to the exponential law $\exp(-\alpha x)$, with

$$\alpha = 2\beta \cdot \frac{\omega n_0}{c}. \tag{24}$$

The quantity α represents the coefficient of absorption per unit length of path, while $4\pi\beta$ is the coefficient of absorption per wave-length in the medium.

If the refractive index does not deviate too much from unity in absolute value (even in the resonance regions), we may write, by (15),

$$\gamma = \sum_k \gamma_k = \frac{3(n^2-1)}{n^2+2} \approx n_0^2 - 1 + \tfrac{1}{3}\beta^2 - 2i\beta. \tag{25}$$

The comparison of (22) and (25) then yields for the refractive index and the absorption coefficient the approximative formulae

$$n_0^2 - 1 \approx N \sum_k \frac{e_k^2}{m_k} \cdot \frac{\omega_k^2 - \omega^2 - \tfrac{1}{6}\beta\omega\Gamma_k}{(\omega_k^2 - \omega^2)^2 + \omega^2\Gamma_k^2}$$

$$2\beta \approx N \sum_k \frac{e_k^2}{m_k} \cdot \frac{\omega\Gamma_k}{(\omega_k^2 - \omega^2)^2 + \omega^2\Gamma_k^2}. \tag{26}$$

In the resonance region ω_k, i.e. for $|\omega_k - \omega| \ll \omega_k$, the term γ_k in the expression for the polarizability is predominant, and the summation may be dropped on the right-hand side of (26). Moreover, we may replace ω by ω_k except in the difference $\omega_k - \omega$, and we get the simpler formulae

$$n_0^2 - 1 \approx N \frac{e_k^2}{2m_k\omega_k} \cdot \frac{\omega_k - \omega - \frac{1}{12}\beta\Gamma_k}{(\omega_k - \omega)^2 + \frac{1}{4}\Gamma_k^2}$$

$$2\beta \approx N \frac{e_k^2}{2m_k\omega_k} \cdot \frac{\frac{1}{2}\Gamma_k}{(\omega_k - \omega)^2 + \frac{1}{4}\Gamma_k^2}.$$

(27)

The graphic representation of these formulae (Figure 5) shows on the one hand the peculiar reversal of the frequency variation

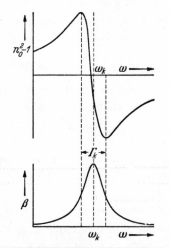

Fig. 5. Anomalous dispersion and absorption

of the refractive index in the resonance region, called *anomalous dispersion*, and on the other hand the strongly selective character of resonance absorption. The *width* of the "absorption line" at $\omega = \omega_k$ is conventionally measured by the quantity Γ_k defined in (22): it is characterized by the fact that for $\omega = \omega_k \pm \frac{1}{2}\Gamma_k$, the absorption coefficient is (approximately) equal to half its maximum value. The extremes of the refractive index on either side of the resonance frequency occur at nearly the same frequencies, so that Γ_k is also the width of the region of anomalous dispersion.

4. RADIATION DAMPING AND EXTINCTION COEFFICIENT

In the preceding theory of absorption the damping of the atomic oscillators has been introduced in a purely formal way, without any reference to the physical mechanism by which such damping is produced. Usually the predominant effect will be the disturbance of the atomic oscillations by collisions or other interactions, which results in a transfer of energy from the oscillatory degrees of freedom to various kinds of disorderly thermal motions, and thus causes true absorption.

Besides this collision damping, however, there is another dissipative reaction on the oscillators, arising from the fact that they radiate electromagnetic energy in the very process of transmitting the incident light through the medium. Since these secondary light waves are emitted in all directions, some energy will in general be taken from the incident wave in the course of its progress through the medium; this energy, however, will not be transformed into heat, but merely scattered in all directions in the form of light: this scattering will give an additional contribution to the *extinction* of the incident light wave, i.e. to its attenuation in passing through the medium. Besides the coefficient of true absorption, considered in the preceding section, we must define a *scattering coefficient* as the fraction of the energy of the incident wave scattered in all directions per unit length of path. According to the picture of the phenomenon just outlined, the total *coefficient of extinction* of the wave is the sum of the scattering coefficient and the coefficient of true absorption.

We have now to enquire into the frictional force exerted on our system of oscillators by its own radiation field. Its expression can be inferred from the condition that the work done by this force during a period of the forced oscillation of the system must be equal to the energy radiated away during this time. For a radiating dipole of moment **p**, the latter quantity is given by the well-known expression $- (6\pi c^3)^{-1} \int \frac{1}{2} |\dddot{\mathbf{p}}|^2 \, dt$, which may be written *

$$- \frac{1}{6\pi c^3} \int \frac{1}{2} \left[\frac{d}{dt} (\ddot{\mathbf{p}} \cdot \dot{\mathbf{p}}_c) - \frac{d^3\mathbf{p}}{dt^3} \cdot \dot{\mathbf{p}}_c \right] dt.$$

The first term vanishes, and the second can be interpreted, since $\dot{\mathbf{p}} \, dt = \sum e_k \, \dot{\mathbf{x}}_k \, dt$, as the work done on the system of vibrating charges by a force equivalent to the electric field

$$\mathbf{e}_r = \frac{1}{6\pi c^3} \frac{d^3\mathbf{p}}{dt^3}, \tag{28}$$

acting on each of them.

A direct derivation of the field (28) has been given by Lorentz **, in a piece of analysis which is one of the most beautiful examples of his masterly, straightforward approach to physical problems. He considers a charged "particle" of finite spatial extension, in accelerated translation, and works out the electromagnetic field produced in the vicinity of such an accelerated "particle". He finds that the component of the electric field in the direction of the motion involves terms of a dissipative character, the most important of which is just of the form (28), viz. $(6\pi c^3)^{-1} e \dddot{\mathbf{x}}$: it is proportional to the total charge of the particle, but quite independent of the spatial distribution of this charge; for sufficiently small distances it is also independent of the distance. If, therefore, we have a system of particles performing harmonic oscillations around the same centre (or neighbouring centres) in the same direction, with amplitudes small compared with the wave-length of the oscillation, the total *radiative reaction* on any one of them will be the sum of contributions of the above type, arising from the particle itself and from all the others, each with its specific factor $e_k \dddot{\mathbf{x}}_k$: this is exactly the conclusion expressed by (28), which in this case may also be written as

$$\mathbf{e}_r = - \frac{i}{6\pi} \left(\frac{\omega}{c} \right)^3 \mathbf{p}. \tag{29}$$

---

* The index c denotes the complex conjugate; the factor $\frac{1}{2}$ arises from the use of complex vectors.

** H. A. Lorentz, *Theory of Electrons* (1909), p. 251.

The influence of the radiative reaction on the dispersion formulae may be studied by inserting the corresponding field $\mathbf{e}_r$, in addition to that of the incident wave, in the relation connecting the induced dipole moment with the latter field:

$$\mathbf{p} = \gamma_a(\mathbf{e} + \mathbf{e}_r),\qquad(30)$$

where γ_a is the molecular polarizability. With the interpretation (15) of the coefficient of polarizability this relation also takes the average interaction of the molecules into account (as described by the internal field). But it must be stressed that it implies the assumption that there is on the average no resultant *dissipative* (or regenerative) action, on a particular molecule, of the radiation fields emitted by the others. We may at any rate expect such a condition to be fulfilled for gases of low density, and we shall therefore expressly restrict the following considerations of the present section to this case. In the next chapter a rigorous theory of dispersion will be developed, in which special attention will be paid to the problem of the radiative interactions of the molecules. According to (22), we might use for the molecular polarizability γ_a in (30) the expression

$$\gamma_a = \sum_k \frac{e_k^2}{m_k} \cdot \frac{1}{\omega_k^2 - \omega^2 + i\omega\varGamma_k},\qquad(31)$$

somewhat more general than (19) inasmuch as it embodies the effect of collision damping. We shall confine the discussion, however, to frequencies ω lying outside the resonance regions, i.e. such that $|\omega_k - \omega| \gg \tfrac{1}{2}\varGamma_k$ for all ω_k: in this case the polarizability γ_a may be regarded as a real quantity, given by (19). The only cause of extinction of the incident wave is then its scattering, and the coefficient of extinction is identical with the scattering coefficient. Inserting the expression (29) for the radiative reaction into (30), we see after some easy transformations that the polarizability per unit volume γ now takes the form

$$\gamma = N\left\{\frac{1}{\gamma_a} + \frac{i}{6\pi}\left(\frac{\omega}{c}\right)^3\right\}^{-1}.\qquad(32)$$

We have therefore only to identify the reciprocal of the right-hand side of this formula with

$$\frac{1}{\gamma} = \frac{n^2+2}{3(n^2-1)} \approx \frac{n_0^2+2}{3(n_0^2-1)} + 2i\beta \frac{n_0^2}{(n_0^2-1)^2};$$

in the last expression no restriction is made concerning the value of n_0, but terms in β^2 and higher powers of β are neglected. For the refractive index we obtain, of course, the same relation as in Section 2 above. For the extinction coefficient a defined by (24) we get the remarkable expression

$$a = \frac{1}{6\pi N} \cdot \left(\frac{\omega}{c}\right)^4 \cdot \frac{(n_0^2-1)^2}{n_0}. \tag{33}$$

As pointed out already, this formula can also be interpreted as giving the scattering coefficient of the gas: it is in this form that it was put forward for the first time by Lord Rayleigh in 1899. For frequencies outside the resonance regions the variation of the refractive index with frequency is much slower than that indicated by the factor ω^4: the scattering or extinction coefficient will thus show a very strong frequency-dependence, practically according to a "fourth-power law". For instance, from the point of view of extinction, this law accounts for the reddening effect of the atmosphere at sunset. Applied to the scattering coefficient, it forms the basis of Lord Rayleigh's famous explanation (1899) of the blue colour of the sky, as due to the scattering of the light from the sun by the molecules of the air.

Still more striking is the explicit appearance in formula (33) of the atomistic quantity N. This implies that an estimate of Avogadro's number can be derived from a study of the scattered light of the sky. The reason for the atomistic character of the law of light scattering is that the damping force in this case is not a statistical average like that due to atomic collisions, but is intimately related to the individual emission processes which determine the phenomenon: the net result of the superposition of these processes is essentially a statistical *fluctuation* effect. In order to see this a much deeper analysis of the dispersion phenomena is required: it will be given in the next chapter. But a direct attack on the *scattering* aspect of the problem, as we will now proceed to show, brings out the part played by fluctuation effects in a simple and instructive manner.

5. SCATTERING OF LIGHT

Let us consider (Figure 6) a beam of light of frequency ω passing through a medium of refractive index n_0 along the direction **t**. If the light is unpolarized we may represent it by the superposition of two incoherent waves, whose electric vectors oscillate in two

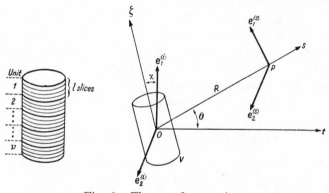

Fig. 6.   Theory of scattering

perpendicular directions normal to **t**, with equal amplitudes $|\mathbf{e}_1^{(i)}| = |\mathbf{e}_2^{(i)}|$. Let us fix our attention on a small volume V of matter at a point O. The electric field of the incident wave will induce oscillating dipole moments in the molecules contained in this volume: these dipoles will radiate coherently, and our first task is to evaluate the radiation field resulting from the superposition of all the secondary waves emitted from the volume V at any point P whose distance R from O is large compared to the dimensions of V. Since we have to do with an unpolarized incident wave, we may choose the point P in the plane ($\mathbf{e}_1^{(i)}$, **t**) in a direction **s** making the angle θ with **t**.

Let $\mathbf{e}^{(i)} \exp i\omega t$ be the electric field of the incident wave at O, with the two incoherent components $\mathbf{e}_1^{(i)}$, $\mathbf{e}_2^{(i)}$, so that

$$\mathbf{e}^{(i)} = \mathbf{e}_1^{(i)} + \mathbf{e}_2^{(i)}.$$

This incident wave must be regarded as progressing in the medium of refractive index n_0; for the energy contained in the volume V we must use the expression given by Maxwell's theory, viz.

$$\tfrac{1}{2} n_0^2 (\,|\mathbf{e}_1^{(i)}|^2 + |\mathbf{e}_2^{(i)}|^2)\, V \tag{34}$$

(the factor $\tfrac{1}{2}$ arises from the time-average of $\cos^2 \omega t$ over a period). The dipole moment induced in a molecule whose distance from the plane $(\mathbf{e}_1^{(i)}, \mathbf{e}_2^{(i)})$ through O is z has the phase $\omega\{t-(n_0/c)z\}$, in accordance with the velocity of propagation of the incident wave c/n_0. Its average amplitude is related to $\mathbf{e}^{(i)}$, according to the interpretation (14) of the refractive index, by $N\mathbf{p} = (n_0^2 - 1)\mathbf{e}^{(i)}$, if N denotes the average number of molecules per unit volume. We have, therefore, for the induced dipole moment

$$\mathbf{p} \exp i\omega\Big(t - \frac{n_0}{c} z\Big), \quad \text{with} \quad \mathbf{p} = \frac{n_0^2 - 1}{N} \mathbf{e}^{(i)}. \tag{35}$$

The secondary waves emitted by these dipoles, on the other hand, are properly treated as "microscopic" events, occurring *in vacuo*. Their electric amplitudes $\mathbf{e}^{(s)}$ may be written, according to Hertz' well-known formulae,

$$
\begin{aligned}
\mathbf{e}_1^{(s)} &= [\mathbf{p}_1 - (\mathbf{p}_1 \cdot \mathbf{s})\,\mathbf{s}] \cdot (\omega/c)^2 \cdot (4\pi R)^{-1} \\
\mathbf{e}_2^{(s)} &= \phantom{[\mathbf{p}_1 - (\mathbf{p}_1}\mathbf{p}_2 \cdot (\omega/c)^2 \cdot (4\pi R)^{-1},
\end{aligned} \tag{36}
$$

the corresponding phases at P being referred to the origin O. These phases are of the form $\omega\{t-(R/c)\} + \varphi_M$, where φ_M is the difference between the phase of the secondary wave emitted from any point M of the volume V and that of the wave emitted from O. Let us select a sequence of phase values $\varphi_1, \varphi_2, \ldots, \varphi_l$ such that any value of φ_M corresponding to a molecule in the volume V may be identified with sufficient accuracy with some particular φ_j; let N_j be the number of molecules in V whose phase is equal to

φ_j within the assigned accuracy. The resultant field of the scattered wave at P due to the molecules in V may then be written

$$\mathbf{e}^{(s)} \, \varPhi \, \exp i\omega \left(t - \frac{R}{c}\right), \quad \text{with} \quad \varPhi = \sum_{j=1}^{l} N_j \exp i\varphi_j. \tag{37}$$

The absolute value of the Poynting vector of the scattered wave, averaged over a period, is, on account of the incoherence of the two components of $\mathbf{e}^{(s)}$,

$$\tfrac{1}{2} c \left(|\mathbf{e}_1^{(s)}|^2 + |\mathbf{e}_2^{(s)}|^2 \right) |\varPhi|^2.$$

The energy scattered per unit time within an element of solid angle $d\Omega$ in the direction $\mathbf{s}$ is obtained by multiplying this expression by $R^2 d\Omega$. If we divide the result by the energy of the incident wave contained in the volume V, and by the velocity of propagation c/n_0 (in order to reduce it to the unit length of path), we get an expression of the form $a(\theta)\, d\Omega$ defining the *differential scattering coefficient* $a(\theta)$. Using (36) and (35), we find

$$a(\theta) = a \cdot \frac{3}{16\pi}\,(1 + \cos^2 \theta) \cdot \frac{|\varPhi|^2}{\overline{N}_V},$$

with

$$a = \frac{1}{6\pi N} \cdot \left(\frac{\omega}{c}\right)^4 \cdot \frac{(n_0^2 - 1)^2}{n_0}; \tag{38}$$

in this formula $\overline{N}_V$ represents the average number NV of molecules in the volume V. We may note that the integration over the angles of the factor $(3/16\pi)\,(1 + \cos^2\theta)$ yields unity. The problem is now reduced to the discussion of the phase factor given by (37). The selection of the phase sequence φ_j is conveniently made in the following way. It is possible to find in the plane $(\mathbf{t}, \mathbf{s})$ a direction $O\zeta$ (making an angle χ with that of $\mathbf{e}_1^{(i)}$) such that the secondary waves emitted from all points of any plane perpendicular to $O\zeta$ have the same phase at the distant point P. An elementary calculation shows that for any scattering angle $\theta\ (\neq 0)$ the corresponding angle χ is defined by the equation

$$n_0 \cos \chi = \cos (\theta - \chi);$$

for $n_0 = 1$, this gives $\chi = \tfrac{1}{2}\theta$, i.e. the line $O\zeta$ bisects the exterior angle of the directions $\mathbf{t}$, $\mathbf{s}$ of incidence and scattering. Let us accordingly choose as our volume V a cylinder of axis $O\zeta$ and height h. For a point of the axis $O\zeta$, at a distance ζ from O, the phase difference is found to be

$$\varphi_\zeta = \frac{2\pi\zeta}{\lambda_\theta}, \quad \text{with} \quad \lambda_\theta = \frac{2\pi c}{\omega} \cdot (n_0^2 + 1 - 2n_0 \cos\theta)^{-\frac{1}{2}}. \quad (39)$$

Except for very small scattering angles *, the quantity λ_θ is of the order of the wave-length $2\pi c/\omega$. We may therefore assume, at any rate for optical frequencies (to which we limit ourselves here), that the small interval h ($\ll R$) contains a large integral number ν of "units" λ_θ. Let us now subdivide each of the corresponding "unit cylinders" into the same sufficiently large number l of equal "slices" of height η, to which we attach the same indices $1, 2, \ldots, l$ in each unit. Clearly, all molecules contained in those slices with the same index j will have the same phase difference $\varphi_j = 2\pi j\eta/\lambda_\theta = 2\pi j/l$ with an error that cannot exceed $2\pi/l$: let the number of such molecules be N_j. We have arrived by this procedure at a precise definition of our phase sequence φ_j and phase factor Φ.

An obvious consequence of this definition is that if all N_j are equal, the phase factor Φ vanishes. This situation occurs if the molecules or atoms are arranged in a regular spatial pattern: *a perfect crystal does not scatter light at all.* More generally, the same conclusion applies to any perfectly homogeneous distribution of matter: this makes it clear that whatever scattering is observed can only be due to deviations from uniformity in the spatial distribution of the molecules, such as are always present in the form of *thermal fluctuations.* If ΔN_j represents the chance deviation of N_j from its average value $\overline{N}_V/l$, we may therefore write for Φ, instead of (37),

$$\Phi = \sum_{j=1}^{l} \Delta N_j \cdot \exp i\varphi_j,$$

and we have to evaluate the statistical average of $|\Phi|^2$, viz.

$$\overline{|\Phi|^2} = \sum_{j,k} \overline{\Delta N_j \, \Delta N_k} \cdot \exp i(\varphi_j - \varphi_k). \quad (40)$$

---

* The case of small-angle scattering would require special consideration, but it will appear that it is of no influence on the total scattering, except for a gas at the critical point (see next section).

For a gas of low density we may neglect all correlations between
different volume elements, and $|\Phi|^2$ reduces to the sum of the
mean square fluctuations $\sum \overline{\Delta N_j^2} = \sum \overline{N_j} = \overline{N}_V$. The factor $|\Phi|^2/\overline{N}_V$
in formula (38) thus reduces to unity, and the total scattering
coefficient $\int a(\theta)\, d\Omega$ takes the value a, identical to the expression
(33) which we found for the extinction coefficient in this case. The
reason for the presence of an uncompensated atomistic factor N
in the denominator of a is now apparent: since the scattering
from a given volume depends on the fluctuation of the number of
molecules in the volume, its intensity is proportional to the mean
value of this number, and not to its square. When the coherence
of the scattered wavelets is fully effective, as in a crystal, there
results a complete destruction by interference of all radiation
outside the direction of incidence. The appearance of scattered
radiation in any other direction is due to the disturbance of the
coherence by the thermal agitation of the sources, and the net
result is the same (in the case of an ideal gas which we are discussing) as if all elements of volume scattered the incident light
incoherently.

Returning to the expression (36) for the electric amplitudes of the
scattered waves, we observe that *the light scattered from an unpolarized incident beam is partially polarized in a direction normal
to the plane formed by the directions of incidence and scattering; if
these two directions are perpendicular, the polarization of the scattered
light is complete* (at any rate for isotropic molecules). The *depolar-
ization* for any angle of scattering, i.e. the ratio of the intensities
of the incoherent components $\mathbf{e}_1^{(s)}$, $\mathbf{e}_2^{(s)}$, is $\cos^2 \theta$. The polarization
of skylight was discovered by Arago in 1811; it can easily be
observed just by looking at the sky through a nicol or a piece of
polaroid. Bees are able to perceive the polarization of skylight and
to use this perception in order to orient themselves with respect
to the sun: they find their bearings even when the sun is hidden
from their view, so long as they receive light from any patch of
blue sky; and the property which enables them to do so is just the
polarization of the sunlight. This amazing fact has been established

by recent experiments of the Austrian biologist K. von Frisch *.
Besides the coherent "Rayleigh scattering" there may be an
incoherent scattering of light with frequencies different from the
incident one. This phenomenon, the "Raman effect", is connected
with an "excitation" of the scattering molecules by the incident
radiation. An extreme case of incoherent scattering which deserves
special mention is that of free electrons. The scattering coefficient
may be obtained from (33) by replacing N by the number N_e of
electrons per unit volume and inserting the value of $n_0^2 - 1$ given
by (21); observing further that, by (21), $n_0 \approx 1$, one gets the
remarkable formula, first derived by J. J. Thomson,

$$a_e \approx N_e \cdot \tfrac{8}{3}\pi r_0^2, \quad \text{with ** } \quad r_0 = \frac{e^2}{4\pi mc^2} = 2.8 \cdot 10^{-13} \text{ cm.} \quad (41)$$

From this expression it appears that each electron scatters light
of all frequencies equally, like an "obstacle" of linear dimensions
of the order of the *classical electron radius* r_0. For atoms, Thomson's
formula may be applied in the limiting case of high frequencies;
historically, it has been of great importance in the early discussions
of the scattering of X-rays by atoms: it yielded for the first time
an estimate of the number Z of constituent electrons in an atom,
viz. about half the atomic weight. An accurate calculation of the
scattering coefficient for X-rays, however, requires the methods
of quantum mechanics: the accompanying change of frequency in
this case, the "Compton effect", is a purely quantal feature.

6. CRITICAL OPALESCENCE

The investigation of the scattering of light by non-ideal gases,
with the help of the complete expression (40) for the phase factor,
is chiefly due to Ornstein and Zernike (1914), who have made a
special study of the peculiar effects occurring near the critical

---

* K. von Frisch, *Experientia*, **5**, 142, 1949; **6**, 210, 1950.

** In computing the numerical value of the *length* r_0 it is necessary to
remember that e in our formulae is expressed in Heaviside units, so that its
numerical value is greater by a factor $\sqrt{(4\pi)}$ than its value in electrostatic
units.

point, and known as *critical opalescence*. The essential features of these phenomena are, of course, determined by the correlations $\overline{\Delta N_j \, \Delta N_k}$ of the density fluctuations in different elements of volume. The connection of these correlations with the thermo-dynamical state of the system, and especially with the critical point, is most clearly shown by the consideration of the density fluctuations in larger volumes, a phenomenon closely related to our problem. We shall therefore begin with a discussion of these fluctuations, and return afterwards to the question of light scattering.

Let us consider, in the interior of the gas, a volume V, containing a fluctuating number N_V of molecules. We subdivide the volume V into a large number of "cells" of volumes dv_j, in which the numbers of molecules N_j will also fluctuate. We may imagine the individual cells so small that the fluctuations within any one of them are perfectly at random, and $\overline{\Delta N_j^2} = \overline{N}_j$. But for the mean square fluctuation of the number N_V of molecules in the total volume V we get

$$\overline{\Delta N_V^2} = \sum_{j,\,k} \overline{\Delta N_j \, \Delta N_k} = \sum_j \overline{\Delta N_j^2} + \sum_{j \neq k} \overline{\Delta N_j \, \Delta N_k}: \qquad (42)$$

besides the additive term $\sum \overline{\Delta N_j^2} = \sum \overline{N}_j = \overline{N}_V$, there occurs a correlation term which accounts for the deviation from the behaviour of an ideal gas. In fact, $\overline{\Delta N_V^2}$ is given in terms of the macroscopic, thermodynamical variables, by the general formula, derived with the help of statistical mechanics,

$$\frac{\overline{\Delta N_V^2}}{\overline{N}_V} = N\,kT\,\beta, \qquad (43)$$

where N is the average number of molecules per unit volume, and

$$\beta = -\frac{1}{V}\left(\frac{\partial V}{\partial p}\right)_T \qquad (44)$$

represents the coefficient of isothermal compressibility. At the critical point this quantity becomes infinite: the comparison of (43) with the statistical expression (42) shows how this singularity is connected with the occurrence of large and strongly correlated density fluctuations. These fluctuations are revealed by the accompanying optical scattering effects, whose intensity is proportional to the phase factor (40).

The correlation $\overline{\Delta N_j \Delta N_k}$ between the density fluctuations in two cells j, k of the volume V may be described by a function $g(r_{jk})$ of the distance between the cells, defined as follows: if the fluctuation in the jth cell has some definite value ΔN_j, it will influence either directly or indirectly the average deviation $\overline{\Delta N_k}$ from the mean number of molecules in the kth cell, in such a way that if we denote by $\overline{\Delta N_k}|_j$ this average deviation, we shall have a relation of the form

$$\overline{\Delta N_k}|_j = g(r_{jk}) \, dv_k \, \Delta N_j \qquad (j \neq k). \tag{45}$$

Now, multiplying both sides of this equation by ΔN_j and taking the average, we get

$$\overline{\Delta N_j \Delta N_k} = g(r_{jk}) \, dv_k \, \overline{\Delta N_j^2} = g(r_{jk}) \, N \, dv_j \, dv_k \quad (j \neq k). \tag{46}$$

Putting *

$$G = \int_V g(r) \, dv, \tag{47}$$

we may therefore write equation (42) in the form

$$\overline{\Delta N_V^2} = \overline{N}_V (1 + G). \tag{48}$$

In order to evaluate the correlation function $g(r)$, another auxiliary function $f(r)$ is introduced by a definition similar to that of $g(r)$, but expressing only the *direct* influence of a given fluctuation at j on the mean number of molecules at k (the indirect effects may be eliminated by imagining that in all other cells the number of molecules is maintained at its average value). With the help of this "direct correlation function" $f(r_{jk})$ the average $\overline{\Delta N_k}$ for any cell may be expressed in the form

$$\overline{\Delta N_k} = \sum_{j \neq k} f(r_{jk}) \, dv_k \, \Delta N_j, \tag{49}$$

---

* The distances r are measured from an arbitrarily selected point in V. It is further assumed that $\lim_{r \to 0} g(r) \, dv = 0$.

when the fluctuations ΔN_j in all other cells are given definite values. Let us now take the average of both sides of (49) on the assumption that the fluctuation ΔN_i in the ith cell has a definite value; this gives

$$\overline{\Delta N_k}|_i = \sum_{j \neq k, i} f(r_{jk}) \, dv_k \, \overline{\Delta N_j}|_i + f(r_{ik}) \, dv_k \, \Delta N_i.$$

Using (45) and dividing by the common factor $dv_k \, \Delta N_i$, we get

$$g(r_{ik}) = \sum_{j \neq k, i} f(r_{jk}) \, g(r_{ij}) \, dv_j + f(r_{ik}),$$

or as an integral equation *

$$g(r) = \int_V f(|\mathbf{r} - \mathbf{r}'|) \, g(r') \, dv' + f(r). \tag{50}$$

According to its physical meaning, the direct correlation function $f(r)$ must be expected to decrease rapidly with increasing distance, i.e. to have a limited "range", even at the critical point. By using this fact, we easily derive from the integral equation (50) a differential equation for $g(r)$, valid for distances r larger than the range of $f(r)$. In fact, for such values of r, we may neglect the second term on the right-hand side of (50); in the first term we may in any case replace $g(r')$ by the first few terms of its Taylor expansion with respect to the point of radius vector $\mathbf{r}$. The term $g(r)$ in this expansion appears multiplied by

$$F = \int_V f(r) \, dv; \tag{51}$$

the next term gives zero owing to the assumed isotropy of the direct correlation function $f(r)$; the second-order term yields $F\varepsilon^2 \triangle g$, where $\triangle$ is the Laplacian operator and

$$\varepsilon^2 = \frac{1}{6F} \int_V r^2 f(r) \, dv. \tag{52}$$

---

* It is also assumed that $\lim_{r \to 0} f(r) \, dv = 0$.

Limiting the expansion at this stage, we get the equation

$$\triangle g - \frac{1}{\varkappa^2}\, g = 0, \tag{53}$$

with $\varkappa^2 = F\varepsilon^2/(1 - F)$. The integral equation (50) yields a relation between F and the quantity G occurring in the density fluctuations and defined by (47): integrating both sides of (50) over the volume V, and observing that the integral F may be regarded as independent of the origin of the radii vectores $\mathbf{r} - \mathbf{r}'$, we find immediately

$$G = FG + F.$$

This relation may be written in various equivalent ways:

$$G = F/(1 - F), \qquad F = G/(1 + G),$$

$$1 + G = \frac{1}{1-F} = \frac{\overline{\varDelta N_V^2}}{\overline{N}_V} = N\,kT\,\beta. \tag{54}$$

In the last formula, reference has been made, for future use, to the preceding relations (48) and (43). It will be noticed that the integral F tends to unity as the critical point is approached. On account of (54) we may write

$$\varkappa^2 = G\varepsilon^2. \tag{55}$$

The solution of (53) which represents the correlation function $g(r)$ at distances larger than the range of $f(r)$ is

$$g(r) = \frac{G}{\varkappa^2} \cdot \frac{e^{-r/\varkappa}}{4\pi\,r}; \tag{56}$$

the constant factor has been chosen in such a way that $\int g(r)\,dv = G$ when the integral is extended over all space *. The parameter $\varkappa$ is the range of the correlation function $g(r)$, just as ε may be

---

* It may be verified that (in the limiting case of $V \to \infty$) the function (56) is an exact solution of the integral equation (50) if we choose for $f(r)$ an expression of similar form

$$f(r) = \frac{F}{\varepsilon^2} \cdot \frac{e^{-r/\varepsilon}}{4\pi\,r};$$

in which case the relation (52) is identically satisfied.

taken as a measure of the range of the direct correlation function $f(r)$: while the latter remains finite, the former, as shown by (55), becomes infinite at the critical point. The normalization factor of the solution (56), however, has the finite value ε^{-2}.

We may now return to the general expression (40) for the phase factor. The $\varDelta N_j$ occurring in it refer to domains consisting of ν separate slices of our small cylinder V; but by an obvious relabelling of the slices, with j running from 1 to νl, we may arrange that $\varDelta N_j$ refers to a single slice. With this new meaning, formula (40) keeps exactly the same form. By transformations similar to those which led from the expression (42) for the density fluctuation to the expression (48), we put $\overline{|\varPhi|^2}$ into the form

$$\frac{\overline{|\varPhi|^2}}{N_V} = 1 + g_\varphi(\theta) \quad \text{with} \quad g_\varphi(\theta) = \int\limits_V g(r)\, e^{2\pi i\zeta/\lambda_\theta}\, dv, \qquad (57)$$

according to the formula (39) for the phase difference φ_ζ. Let us assume, for simplicity, that the scattering volume V is a sphere of radius R. With a suitable choice of polar co-ordinates, such that $\zeta = r \cos\theta'$, the angular integration in g_φ can then be immediately effected, and with the help of the expression (39) for λ_θ, its result may be written

$$g_\varphi(\theta) = 4\pi \int\limits_0^R g(r)\, r^2\, dr\, j_0\{\sigma r \sqrt{(n_0^2 + 1 - 2n_0 \cos\theta)}\} \qquad (58)$$

with

$$j_0(z) = \sin z/z\,;$$

we have put for brevity $\sigma \equiv \omega/c$.

By (38) and (57), the *differential scattering coefficient* is given by

$$a(\theta) = a \cdot \frac{3}{16\pi}\, (1 + \cos^2\theta)\, \{1 + g_\varphi(\theta)\}, \qquad (59)$$

where $g_\varphi(\theta)$ is defined by (58), and a represents Rayleigh's expression (33) for the scattering coefficient of an ideal gas. The *total scattering coefficient* is accordingly

$$a' = a\,(1 + G_\varphi) \quad \text{with} \quad G_\varphi = \tfrac{3}{8} \int\limits_1^1 (1 + \cos^2\theta)\, g_\varphi(\theta)\, d(\cos\theta). \qquad (60)$$

Before attempting an exact evaluation of the quantities $g_\varphi(\theta)$ and G_φ it will be useful to discuss the physical implications of the above formulae in the simple limiting case in which the correlation range $\varkappa$ is small compared with the wave-length, i.e. $\varkappa\sigma \ll 1$. We may then replace in (58) $j_0(z)$ by its power series expansion and let $R \to \infty$. The first approximation simply gives $g_\varphi(\theta) \approx G_\varphi \approx G$, and on account of (54) the formulae (59), (60) therefore reduce to

$$a(\theta) \approx a' \cdot \frac{3}{16\pi} \left(1 + \cos^2 \theta\right)$$

$$a' \approx a \cdot \frac{\overline{\Delta N_V^2}}{\overline{N_V}} = \frac{1}{6\pi} \left(\frac{\omega}{c}\right)^4 \cdot \frac{(n_0^2 - 1)^2}{n_0} \cdot kT\beta. \qquad (61)$$

These formulae show that the direct connection between the scattering process and the density fluctuations is not confined to ideal gases, but has a much wider domain of validity. It accounts for the striking display of "flickering striae" appearing in the gas in the neighbourhood of the critical point, described for the first time by Andrews (1863).

The next step requires the assumption of some explicit expression, such as (56), for the correlation function $g(r)$. With (56) and $j_0(z) \approx 1 - \frac{1}{6} z^2$, formula (58) yields

$$g_\varphi(\theta) \approx G \left\{1 - \varkappa^2 \sigma^2(n_0^2 + 1 - 2 n_0 \cos \theta)\right\},$$

whence

$$G_\varphi \approx G \left\{1 - \varkappa^2 \sigma^2(n_0^2 + 1)\right\}.$$

By means of (54), (55), the corresponding approximate values of $1 + g_\varphi$ and $1 + G_\varphi$ can be expressed in terms of the constant ε^2 and the density fluctuation $\overline{\Delta N_V^2}/\overline{N_V}$ or $NkT\beta$. We write down the result only for the total scattering coefficient:

$$a' = a \cdot NkT\beta \left\{1 + 2\varepsilon^2 \sigma^2(n_0^2 + 1) - NkT\beta \cdot \varepsilon^2 \sigma^2(n_0^2 + 1)\right\}, \quad (62)$$

an expression somewhat more accurate than (61). We can also write it in the form

$$\frac{1}{a'} = \frac{1}{a} \left\{\frac{1 - 2\varepsilon^2 \sigma^2(n_0^2 + 1)}{NkT\beta} + \varepsilon^2 \sigma^2(n_0^2 + 1)\right\}. \qquad (63)$$

Now, when the temperature tends to the critical value T_c, the density fluctuation $NkT\beta$ tends to infinity approximately as $(T - T_c)^{-1}$. In fact, using for example van der Waals' equation of state, and assuming that the density has its critical value, one finds

$$N k T \beta = \frac{4}{9} \cdot \frac{T}{T - T_c}. \tag{64}$$

On account of (63) and (64) we therefore expect the scattering coefficient in the neighbourhood of the critical point (so long as $\varkappa\sigma \ll 1$) to vary approximately according to a law of the form

$$\frac{1}{a'} \approx A(T - T_c) + B,$$

which is in good agreement with Zernike's measurements (1915).

We shall now proceed to establish an expression for the total scattering coefficient a', valid for any order of magnitude of the correlation range $\varkappa$, and in fact for any form of the correlation function $g(r)$. To this end we first observe that the function $j_0(z)$ (as expressed by this notation) belongs to a set $j_m(z)$ related to the Bessel functions of half-integral index by the formula

$$j_m(z) = (\pi/2z)^{1/2} J_{m+\frac{1}{2}}(z); \tag{65}$$

these functions are often met with in optical problems. For the particular type of argument of $j_0(z)$ occurring in (58), we have the *addition theorem* (W 11.4 – 3) *

$$j_0 \{\sigma r \sqrt{(n_0^2 + 1 - 2n_0 \cos\theta)}\} = \sum_{m=0}^{\infty} (2m+1) j_m(\sigma r) j_m(\sigma n_0 r) P_m(\cos\theta), \tag{66}$$

representing an expansion of the function on the left-hand side in terms of Legendre polynomials $P_m(\cos\theta)$. If we therefore write

$$\tfrac{3}{4}(1 + \cos^2\theta) = P_0(\cos\theta) + \tfrac{1}{2} P_2(\cos\theta),$$

---

* The symbol (W 11.4 – 3) refers to formula (3) of section 11.4 of G. N. Watson's *Treatise on the Theory of Bessel Functions* (Cambridge, 1922; 2nd edition, 1944). A similar notation, with the sign W&W, will be used in references to E. T. Whittaker and G. N. Watson's *Course of Modern Analysis* (Cambridge, 4th edition, 1927).

and make use of the orthogonality and normalization properties of the Legendre polynomials (W&W 15.14), we immediately derive from (58), (60) and (66) the formula

$$G_\varphi = 4\pi \int_0^R g(r)\, r^2\, dr\, \{j_0(\sigma r)\, j_0(\sigma n_0 r) + \tfrac{1}{2} j_2(\sigma r)\, j_2(\sigma n_0 r)\}, \qquad (67)$$

which, inserted in (60), yields an expression of quite general validity for the scattering coefficient a'.

If we assume the form (56) of the correlation function $g(r)$, and extend the radial integration to infinity, we can evaluate G_φ by making use of the Lipschitz–Hankel formula (W 13.22-2), which in our notation may be written

$$\int_0^\infty e^{-r/\varkappa}\, r\, dr\, j_m(\sigma r)\, j_m(\sigma n_0 r) = (2\sigma^2 n_0)^{-1}\, Q_m(u); \qquad (68)$$

here, $Q_u(u)$ represents a Legendre function of the second kind (W&W 15.3) of the argument

$$u = \{1 + \varkappa^2 \sigma^2(n_0^2 + 1)\}/2\varkappa^2 \sigma^2 n_0. \qquad (69)$$

Thus, taking account of (55), we get

$$G_\varphi = (2\,\varepsilon^2 \sigma^2 n_0)^{-1}\, \{Q_0(u) + \tfrac{1}{2} Q_2(u)\}. \qquad (70)$$

With the explicit expressions (W&W 15.32-Ex. 1) for the Legendre functions, the scattering coefficient is finally obtained in the form *

$$a' = a\left[1 + \frac{3}{8\,\varepsilon^2 \sigma^2 n_0}\left\{\tfrac{1}{2}(u^2 + 1)\log\left(\frac{u+1}{u-1}\right) - u\right\}\right], \qquad (71)$$

where u is defined by (69).

* Of course, if the correlation function (56) is assumed from the start, the expressions (58) for $g_\varphi(\theta)$ and (60) for G_φ can be worked out directly by elementary calculations. In fact, one obtains immediately

$$g_\varphi = G/\{1 + \varkappa^2\sigma^2(n_0^2+1-2n_0\cos\theta)\}$$

whence (71) is derived without difficulty. The procedure developed in the text has the advantage of greater generality.

For small values of $\varkappa\sigma$, i.e. large values of u, the quantity between curly brackets reduces to $\frac{4}{3}\,u^{-1}$, and we are again led to formula (63). For large values of $\varkappa\sigma$, on the other hand, we may neglect the first term of (71) and in the second term replace u by $(n_0^2 + 1)/2n_0$ everywhere except under the logarithm sign. With the value (33) of α, the scattering coefficient becomes in this case

$$a' \approx \frac{1}{8\pi N} \left(\frac{\omega}{c}\right)^2 \left(\frac{n_0^2-1}{n_0}\right)^2 \frac{1}{\varepsilon^2} \cdot$$

$$\left[\frac{1}{2}\left\{\left(\frac{n_0^2+1}{2n_0}\right)^2 + 1\right\} \cdot \log\left\{\frac{1+\varkappa^2\,\sigma^2(n_0+1)^2}{1+\varkappa^2\,\sigma^2(n_0-1)^2}\right\} - \frac{n_0^2+1}{2n_0}\right]. \tag{72}$$

For $n_0 \approx 1$, this reduces to the simpler form

$$a' \approx \frac{1}{\pi N} \left(\frac{\omega}{c}\right)^2 (n_0 - 1)^2 \frac{1}{\varepsilon^2} \left\{\log\frac{2\varkappa\omega}{c} - \frac{1}{2}\right\}. \tag{73}$$

These formulae exhibit the occurrence of a remarkable change in the phenomenon when the correlation range $\varkappa$ becomes larger than the wave-length. In fact, owing to the slow variation of the logarithm, the frequency dependence of a' is actually determined by the factor $(\omega/c)^2$: it has changed from a 4th-power to a 2nd-power law; the scattered light becomes "whiter" in the immediate neighbourhood of the critical point. This effect, which has been verified experimentally by Andant (1924), may be related to a similar modification of the frequency dependence pointed out by Mie in his well-known theory of the scattering of electromagnetic radiation by rigid spherical bodies: the transition from the 4th-power to the 2nd-power law is determined in this case by the decreasing ratio of the wave-length to the radius of the sphere. As the correlation range increases, larger and larger volumes of the gas behave with respect to the light as quasi-rigid bodies. The change in frequency dependence is due to the replacement in the expression for the scattering coefficient of a factor $(\omega/c)^2$ by the quantity $1/\varepsilon^2$. This means that the intensity of scattered light is considerably increased near the critical point, since the direct correlation range ε is of the order of intermolecular distances

($\varepsilon \approx 10^{-7}$ cm), which are very much smaller than the optical wave-lengths.

Strictly speaking, formula (71) is not applicable at the critical point itself, where $\varkappa \to \infty$. For $n_0 \approx 1$, the approximate expression (73) for the scattering coefficient would even become infinite, corresponding to the fact that * $g_\varphi \approx G/\{1 + (2\varkappa\sigma \sin \frac{1}{2}\theta)^2\}$ would then diverge for small angles of scattering **. In this case it will in fact no longer be permissible to make use of the limiting value of $g_\varphi(\theta)$ for an infinite scattering volume, since the correlation extends over the whole volume occupied by the scattering substance. We must rather, in formula (58), keep the upper limit of radial integration R finite and replace the correlation function $g(r)$ by its limiting form for infinite range; according to (56), this is just the constant ε^{-2}. We get in this way

$$[g_\varphi(\theta)]_{\text{crit}} = \frac{1 - \cos\left\{R\sigma\sqrt{(n_0^2+1-2n_0\cos\theta)}\right\}}{\varepsilon^2\,\sigma^2\,(n_0^2+1-2n_0\cos\theta)}; \qquad (74)$$

R is the radius of the vessel (assumed of spherical shape) containing the scattering substance. The value (74) of $g_\varphi(\theta)$ gives rise to a finite scattering coefficient, which, however, will depend explicitly on the dimensions of the container; this is an obvious consequence of the fact that the correlation range is infinite. For $n_0 \approx 1$, e.g., a straightforward calculation leads for the scattering coefficient α' to an expression of the same form as (73), except that the argument of the logarithm is now $(2R\omega/c)e^\gamma$, where $\gamma = 0.5772$ denotes Euler's constant. Thus, formula (73) goes over into the expression valid for the critical point when the correlation range becomes of the same order of magnitude as the dimensions of the container. It should be stressed, however, that this case is purely academic, since, according to (54), (55) and (64),

$$\varkappa^2 \approx \varepsilon^2 \cdot \frac{\frac{4}{9}T_c}{T-T_c} \approx \frac{10^{-12}\ \text{cm}^2\cdot\text{degree}}{T-T_c}\ :$$

---

*   Cf. the preceding footnote.

**   This circumstance has caused much confusion, and the situation was eventually cleared up, as explained in the text, by G. Placzek, *Physik. Z.*, 31, 1052, 1930.

i.e. in order to have a correlation range of the order of 1 cm, the temperature should not differ from the critical value by more than 10^{-12} degree! The actually observable phenomena are adequately described by Ornstein and Zernike's formulae (61), (63) and (73), which are special cases of the general expression (71).

CHAPTER VI

RIGOROUS THEORY OF DISPERSION

The elementary theory of dispersion developed in the preceding chapter is inadequate in its summary treatment of the averaging over the spatial distribution of the molecules, which essentially limits its validity to the case of an ideal gas. Moreover, it takes for granted the very existence of an average polarization of the medium, which is less obvious in the optical case than in the case of a uniform external field, in view of the delicate mechanism by which the polarization is set up as a result of interference between the incident radiation and the secondary wavelets emitted by the molecules. A careful analysis of this mechanism is required in order to bring out, on the one hand, the formation of the transmitted wave by polarization of the medium, and on the other hand the effect of the molecular distribution in determining the relative amounts of direct transmission and scattering of the incident light.

A complete treatment of the problem, covering the most general type of crystal structure, would include an explanation of birefringence and dichroism. But from our point of view these finer features are comparatively inessential. To present the main line of argument as clearly as possible we will confine ourselves to the simple case in which the molecules are either distributed isotropically or arranged on the points of a cubic lattice: the same method applies to both cases *. Even so, a certain amount of complication is inherent in the problem; but the argument is perfectly straightforward, and the physical relations disclosed by the analysis are such as to make the theory one of the most beautiful of natural philosophy.

---

* For the presentation adopted in this chapter I am greatly indebted to H. Hoek's doctor thesis, *Algemeene theorie der optische activiteit van isotrope media* (Leiden, 1939).

The first stage (Sections 1 and 2) consists in showing that the interference mechanism referred to above leads to an average polarization $\mathbf{P}$ of the medium, determined by an integral equation of the type

$$\mathbf{P} = \gamma(\mathbf{e}_0 + \mathbf{E}_d), \qquad (a)$$

in which $\mathbf{e}_0$ denotes the incident wave and $\mathbf{E}_d$ represents the field exerted on any molecule of the medium by the dipoles induced in all the other molecules; $\mathbf{E}_d$ is accordingly given in terms of the polarization $\mathbf{P}$ by an integral expression. The polarizability γ is a complex quantity, embodying the dissipative influence of the radiation damping and the inhomogeneity of the molecular distribution.

We next proceed to show that the polarization $\mathbf{P}$ satisfies a wave equation of the type

$$\triangle\mathbf{P} + n^2(\omega/c)^2\,\mathbf{P} = 0, \qquad (b)$$

with a parameter n provisionally left undetermined, and eventually to be identified with the complex refractive index of the medium; besides, $\mathbf{P}$ must fulfil a condition of transversality

$$\operatorname{div}\,\mathbf{P} = 0. \qquad (c)$$

The method of proof consists in assuming the validity of the equations (b) and (c) and transforming the fundamental integral equation (a) so as to establish, eventually, its compatibility with the equations (b) and (c), provided that the parameter n is suitably chosen.

This is most easily done for the transversality condition (c) (Section 3). The essential step of the whole argument then follows (Section 4). It consists in showing that the dipole field $\mathbf{E}_d$ can be analysed into two components, one of which satisfies the wave equation for the vacuum (like the incident wave $\mathbf{e}_0$), while the other is just

$$\frac{n^2 + 2}{3\,(n^2 - 1)}\,\mathbf{P}$$

and accordingly obeys equation (b). It is clear that if we insert this expression for $\mathbf{E}_d$ into equation (a), the first-named component of $\mathbf{E}_d$ must cancel the incident wave, and that equation (a) is identically satisfied if we put

$$\gamma = \frac{3\,(n^2-1)}{n^2+2}\,. \qquad\qquad (d)$$

The concluding step in the argument (Section 4) is the evaluation of the average electric field $\mathbf{E}$ at any point of the medium. It is found that

$$\mathbf{E} = \frac{1}{n^2-1}\,\mathbf{P}, \qquad\qquad (e)$$

which shows that $\mathbf{E}$ satisfies the same equations (b) and (c) as $\mathbf{P}$: these equations are characteristic of a transverse wave of complex refractive index n. With this interpretation of n, formula (d) is seen to express the Lorentz–Lorenz relation, from which refractive inde xand extinction coefficient can be computed (Section 5).

The most remarkable feature revealed by this analysis is certainly the cancellation, or extinction, of the incident wave at any point of the medium by part of the field of the induced dipoles, and the building up of another wave in its stead, propagated with a different phase velocity. The statement of this result, which is the keystone of the theory of dispersion, is known as the *extinction theorem*; it is due to Ewald (1912) and Oseen (1915).

1.   THE AVERAGE POLARIZATION

We must first analyse the way in which an average polarization of the medium is set up under the combined influence of the incident light wave and the radiation fields emitted by the dipoles induced in the molecules of the medium. The dipole moment $\mathbf{p}\exp i\omega t$ induced in a molecule by an electric field $\mathbf{e}\exp i\omega t$ is given by the relation

$$\mathbf{p} = \gamma_a\,\mathbf{e}, \qquad\qquad (1)$$

with a coefficient of molecular polarizability given by (V, 31), or (outside the resonance regions) by (V, 19). The total field $\mathbf{e}$ acting on any molecule is composed of three parts:

$$\mathbf{e} = \mathbf{e}_0 + \mathbf{e}_r + \mathbf{e}_d; \qquad\qquad (2)$$

$\mathbf{e}_0$ is the field of the incident wave (*in vacuo*), $\mathbf{e}_r$ the radiative reaction of the dipole $\mathbf{p}$ upon itself, given by (V, 29), while finally $\mathbf{e}_d$ is the field due to the dipole moments induced in all the other molecules.

For the time being it is sufficient to note that the field produced at P by a dipole situated at P' is a linear function of the components of the dipole moment $\mathbf{p}(P')$. We may write it $\mathsf{F}(P, P') \cdot \mathbf{p}(P')$ by means of a symmetrical tensor $\mathsf{F}(P, P')$. If we consider an assembly of molecules situated at the points $P_0, P_1, P_2, \ldots$ and fix our attention on the molecule at P_0, say, we may therefore write for the "dipole field" at P_0

$$\mathbf{e}_d(P_0) = \sum_i{}' \mathsf{F}(P_0, P_i) \cdot \mathbf{p}(P_i); \tag{3}$$

the sign $\sum'$ indicates that the point P_0 must be excepted from the summation.

From (1), (2), (3) and (V, 29) we derive a set of linear equations connecting all dipole moments $\mathbf{p}(P_j)$ with the values $\mathbf{e}_0(P_j)$ of the field of the incident wave at the points P_j occupied by the molecules:

$$\mathbf{p}(P_0) = \gamma_a \left\{ \mathbf{e}_0(P_0) - \frac{i}{6\pi} \left(\frac{\omega}{c}\right)^3 \mathbf{p}(P_0) + \sum_i{}' \mathsf{F}(P_0, P_i) \cdot \mathbf{p}(P_i) \right\}. \tag{4}$$

This system may be solved by successive approximations according to the scheme

$$\mathbf{p}^{(0)}(P_0) = \gamma_a\, \mathbf{e}_0(P_0)$$

$$\mathbf{p}^{(n)}(P_0) = \gamma_a \left\{ \sum_i{}' \mathsf{F}(P_0, P_i) \cdot \mathbf{p}^{(n-1)}(P_i) - \frac{i}{6\pi} \left(\frac{\omega}{c}\right)^3 \mathbf{p}^{(n-1)}(P_0) \right\} \tag{5}$$

$$\mathbf{p}(P_0) = \sum_{n=0}^{\infty} \mathbf{p}^{(n)}(P_0).$$

In view of the smallness of the parameter γ_a, there is no difficulty in assuming that this iteration procedure converges. It remains to be seen, however, whether the averaging over a physically infinitesimal volume element can be combined with it so as to yield a well-defined value of the average polarization $\mathbf{P}(P)$ at any point of the medium.

The formal proof of this fact has physical implications of considerable importance, which are well worth the labour that it requires. On the one hand, its general physical significance is to show that the intricate interplay of the radiation fields set up in the medium by the incident wave does indeed lead to a stationary state characterized by an average polarization of the medium. On the other hand, the analysis throws light on the origin of the dissipative effects in different physical states of the medium: their increase in the gaseous state with increasing deviation from the ideal condition, as well as their disappearance in the crystalline state.

The argument, naturally suggested by the iteration scheme (5), will be one of complete induction. We will assume that the wavelength of the incident light is large compared with the dimensions of physically infinitesimal volume elements (a condition easily fulfilled for optical wave-lengths outside the domain of X-rays). This will allow us to attribute to the field of the incident wave a constant value $\mathbf{e}_0(P)$ within the physically infinitesimal volume element surrounding the point P. The definition of the average $\mathbf{P}^{(0)}(P)$ for the initial approximation is then immediate:

$$\mathbf{P}^{(0)}(P) = N\gamma_a\,\mathbf{e}_0(P). \tag{6}$$

The next step will be to show that if the $(n-1)$-th average correction term $\mathbf{P}^{(n-1)}(P)$ is assumed to exist, the above iteration formula for $\mathbf{p}^{(n)}$ allows us to define the nth correction term $\mathbf{P}^{(n)}$.

The summation over all dipoles surrounding the point P_0, which occurs in the expression (5) for $\mathbf{p}^{(n)}$, requires some care. It is most easily effected for those points P_i which are sufficiently far from P_0, say outside a sphere $S(P_0)$ of centre P_0, whose radius is of the order of a wave-length. We shall therefore divide the domain of summation into two parts: the first, or "outer domain," is comprised between the sphere $S(P_0)$ and the boundary Σ of the body; the second, or "inner domain," includes the dipoles, other than that at P_0, situated inside the sphere $S(P_0)$: in order to exclude the dipole at P_0 from the summation we must surround it by another sphere $s(P_0)$, so small that it cannot contain any other dipole, and limit the summation to the domain comprised between the two spheres $S(P_0)$ and $s(P_0)$.

Consider now a physically infinitesimal volume element dv' of the outer domain. The contributions from the dipoles contained in dv' to the sum in (5) may all be replaced by the same value $\mathsf{F}(P_0, P') \cdot \mathbf{p}^{(n-1)}(P')$ corresponding to one of them, situated at P'. If $N(P')dv'$ is the actual number of dipoles in dv', the total contribution of the outer domain to the sum in (5) may be replaced by the integral

$$\gamma_a \int\limits_{S(P_0)}^{\Sigma} \overline{N(P')\,dv'}\big|_{P_0}\, \mathsf{F}(P_0, P') \cdot \overline{\mathbf{p}^{(n-1)}(P')}\,, \qquad (7)$$

in which the bar over $\mathbf{p}^{(n-1)}(P')$ indicates an averaging over the irregular "microscopic" variations of this quantity in dv', while $\overline{N(P')\,dv'}\big|_{P_0}$ denotes the statistical average of the number of dipoles in dv' when a dipole is known to occupy the position P_0 (this notation is analogous to that used in Chapter V, Section 6). The expression (7) must finally be averaged over a physically infinitesimal volume element dv surrounding P_0, and accordingly entirely contained within the sphere $S(P_0)$: to do this we merely have to multiply the expression (7) by the actual number of dipoles contained in dv, which we may denote by $N(P_0)\,dv$, and take the statistical average of the result, reduced to unit volume.

If the medium is in the gaseous state, we may use the notation (V, 45) and the relation (V, 46) for the density correlations, and if the mean density N is assumed to be uniform, we may write

$$\frac{1}{dv}\, \overline{N(P_0)\,dv \cdot \overline{N(P')\,dv'}}\big|_{P_0} = N^2\,dv' + N\,g(r)\,dv'\,, \qquad (8)$$

where r is the distance from P' to P_0. In the case of a regular arrangement of the molecules at the points of a cubic lattice *,

---

* The following argument, leading to the relation $1 + G = 0$, may be applied to any type of lattice, provided that a more general correlation function $g(\mathbf{r})$ is introduced.

we may still use the same formula, but the correlation function $g(r)$ is here negative,¦ and its integral over space * G, defined by (V, 47), is equal to -1: for if we consider a domain comprised within a sphere of very large radius, with the exclusion of a small sphere surrounding the centre, the integral G represents the difference between the numbers of molecules contained in such a domain, whose centre is occupied by a molecule, and in an equal domain taken at random in the lattice. According to (V, 48), the relation $1 + G = 0$ expresses the absence of density fluctuations in such a lattice.

With the help of formula (8), the contribution of the outer domain to the average of $\mathbf{p}^{(n)}$ over dv is thus entirely expressed in terms of the average correction term $\mathbf{P}^{(n-1)}$, viz.

$$N \gamma_a \int_{s(P_0)}^{\Sigma} \mathsf{F}(P_0, P') \cdot \mathbf{P}^{(n-1)}(P')\, dv' + \gamma_a \int_{s(P_0)}^{\Sigma} g(r)\, \mathsf{F}(P_0, P') \cdot \mathbf{P}^{(n-1)}(P')\, dv'. \quad (9)$$

It must be noted that while the first term of (9) is of macroscopic character, the second, in conformity with its connection with the density correlation, still contains essentially the molecular parameter γ_a.

The preceding argument cannot be applied to the inner domain, since the contributions from all the dipoles of a volume element dv' in this domain may not be regarded as equal. This difficulty can be circumvented by first averaging over the physically infinitesimal volume element dv surrounding P_0. For each of the dipoles contained in dv we have to perform the same operation, viz. to evaluate the sum of the contributions $\gamma_a\, \mathsf{F}(P_0, P_i) \cdot \mathbf{p}^{(n-1)}(P_i)$ from all the dipoles contained in the inner domain belonging to that particular dipole. The inner domains of summation relating to any two points P_0 of dv can be brought into coincidence by a translation, which establishes a point-to-point correspondence between them. Let us fix our attention, in the domain belonging

---

* The assumption, made in Chapter V, that $g(r)\, dv \to 0$ as $r \to 0$ is equivalent to excluding a small sphere $s(P)$ surrounding P from the domain of integration: the latter procedure is more convenient for our present argument.

to P_0, on a very small element of volume $dv(\mathbf{q})$, containing at most one dipole, whose position is defined by the radius vector $\mathbf{q}$ from P_0: the decisive fact is now that the operator $\mathsf{F}(P_0, P_i)$ is completely defined by the radius vector $\mathbf{q}$ joining P_i to P_0, and is

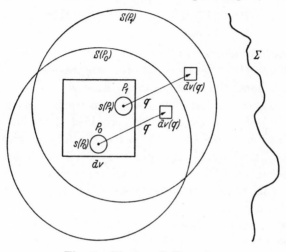

Fig. 7.   Theory of dispersion

therefore the same for all the volume elements $dv(\mathbf{q})$ corresponding to each other by the translation just mentioned. For each radius vector $\mathbf{q}$ the contribution to the average over dv will thus be

$$\frac{1}{dv}\, \gamma_a\, \mathsf{F}(\mathbf{q}) \cdot \sum_{\{dv(\mathbf{q})\}} \overline{\mathbf{p}^{(n-1)}(P')}\,,$$

the sum being extended over the dipoles contained in all the corresponding volume elements $dv(\mathbf{q})$. The average values of $\mathbf{p}^{(n-1)}(P')$ pertain to a physically infinitesimal volume element dv' obtained from dv by the translation of radius vector $\mathbf{q}$; they may accordingly all be taken equal to $\mathbf{P}^{(n-1)}(P')/N$, P' being some point arbitrarily chosen in dv'. It only remains to compute the average number of terms in the sum over the elements $dv(\mathbf{q})$; by the same argument as above, it is

$$N^2\, dv(\mathbf{q})\, dv + N g(q)\, dv(\mathbf{q})\, dv.$$

We must therefore integrate the expression

$$\{N\gamma_a\, \mathsf{F}(\mathbf{q}) \cdot \mathbf{P}^{(n-1)}(P') + \gamma_a\, g(q)\, \mathsf{F}(\mathbf{q}) \cdot \mathbf{P}^{(n-1)}(P')\}\, dv(\mathbf{q})$$

Ewalt

over the inner domain belonging to some arbitrarily selected point P_0 of dv; this integration may obviously be written in the form

$$N \gamma_a \int\limits_{s(P_0)}^{S(P_0)} \mathbf{F}(P_0, P') \cdot \mathbf{P}^{(n-1)}(P') \, dv' + \gamma_a \int\limits_{s(P_0)}^{S(P_0)} g(r) \mathbf{F}(P_0, P') \cdot \mathbf{P}^{(n-1)}(P') dv', \quad (10)$$

which is entirely similar to (9).

Adding (9) and (10) together, and observing that the second term on the right-hand side of (5) can be averaged immediately, we arrive at the conclusion that the nth correction term $\mathbf{p}^{(n)}$ has indeed a well-defined average $\mathbf{P}^{(n)}$, provided that the existence of $\mathbf{P}^{(n-1)}$ is assumed. Since the existence of the initial approximation $\mathbf{P}^{(0)}$ is established by (6), we prove by complete induction the existence of all correction terms of arbitrary order, and (granted the convergence of the series) the existence of the average polarization $\mathbf{P}(P)$ at any point.

The formulae, entirely similar to (5), defining this average polarization, are

$$\mathbf{P}^{(0)}(P) = N \gamma_a \, \mathbf{e}_0(P)$$

$$\mathbf{P}^{(n)}(P) = N \gamma_a \int\limits_{s(P)}^{\Sigma} \mathbf{F}(P, P') \cdot \mathbf{P}^{(n-1)}(P') \, dv_{,}$$

$$+ \gamma_a \left\{ \int\limits_{s(P)}^{\Sigma} g(r) \, \mathbf{F}(P, P') \cdot \mathbf{P}^{(n-1)}(P') \, dv' - i \cdot \frac{1}{6\pi} \left(\frac{\omega}{c} \right)^3 \mathbf{P}^{(n-1)}(P) \right\} \quad (11)$$

$$\mathbf{P}(P) = \sum_{n=0}^{\infty} \mathbf{P}^{(n)}(P).$$

From them one immediately deduces an integral equation connecting the average polarization to the electric field of the incident wave:

$$\mathbf{P}(P) = N \gamma_a \left\{ \mathbf{e}_0(P) + \int\limits_{s(P)}^{\Sigma} \mathbf{F}(P, P') \cdot \mathbf{P}(P') \, dv' \right\}$$

$$+ \gamma_a \left\{ -i \cdot \frac{1}{6\pi} \left(\frac{\omega}{c} \right)^3 \mathbf{P}(P) + \int\limits_{s(P)}^{\Sigma} g(r) \, \mathbf{F}(P, P') \cdot \mathbf{P}(P') dv' \right\}. \quad (12)$$

2. THE AVERAGE POLARIZABILITY

Our next aim is to show that this equation has a solution $\mathbf{P}(P)$ satisfying a wave equation of the type

$$\triangle \mathbf{P} + n^2 \sigma^2 \mathbf{P} = 0, \tag{13}$$

with the accessory condition

$$\text{div } \mathbf{P} = 0. \tag{14}$$

In formula (13) $\sigma \equiv \omega/c$ and n is a provisionally undetermined constant, which will eventually be identified with the (complex) refractive index of the medium. The method we will follow consists in using the *assumptions* (13), (14) to reduce the integrals occurring in (12) to simpler forms; it will then become apparent that the constant n can be chosen in such a way that (12) becomes an identity. We start with the reduction of the last term of (12), which will lead us to the general expression for the average polarizability of the medium.

In order to evaluate the integral in the last term of equation (12) we need the explicit expression for the electric field produced at P by a dipole situated at P'. To this end we start from the Green's function for retarded potentials

$$U(P, P') = \frac{1}{4\pi r} \exp\left(-i\sigma r\right), \tag{15}$$

belonging to the equation of propagation of monochromatic waves *in vacuo*

$$\triangle U + \sigma^2 U = 0. \tag{16}$$

With the help of the Hertz vector $\mathbf{P}(P') \, U(P, P')$, the electric field at P is expressed by

$$\mathsf{F}(P, P') \cdot \mathbf{P}(P') \equiv \text{curl curl } \mathbf{P}(P') \, U(P, P'), \tag{17}$$

the operation curl being performed with respect to the point P.

It will be convenient, in carrying out this computation, to make use of a representation of the Green's function U by a Hankel function (W 3.6) of the argument $\zeta = \sigma r$. Let us introduce the set of functions

$$h_m^{(2)}(\zeta) = \left(\frac{\pi}{2\zeta}\right)^{\frac{1}{2}} H_{m+\frac{1}{2}}^{(2)}(\zeta)$$

analogous to (V, 65); with this notation we have $U = (\sigma/4\pi i) h_0^{(2)}(\zeta)$. Using the relations (W 3.6 – 10)

$$\frac{d}{d\zeta} h_0^{(2)} = - h_1^{(2)} , \qquad \frac{d}{d\zeta} (\zeta^{-1} h_1^{(2)}) = - \zeta^{-1} h_2^{(2)} ,$$

and denoting by $\mathbf{r}^0$ the unit vector in the direction from P to P', we get * from (17)

$$\mathsf{F}(P, P') \cdot \mathbf{P}(P') = \frac{\sigma}{4\pi i} \cdot \sigma^2 \{ (h_0^{(2)} - \zeta^{-1} h_1^{(2)}) \, \mathbf{P}_{P'} + h_2^{(2)}(\mathbf{P}_{P'} \cdot \mathbf{r}^0) \, \mathbf{r}^0 \}.$$

Eliminating $h_1^{(2)}$ by the recurrence relation (W 3.6 – 3)

$$3 \zeta^{-1} h_1^{(2)} = h_0^{(2)} + h_2^{(2)}$$

we have

$$\mathsf{F}(P, P') \cdot \mathbf{P}(P') = \frac{\sigma^3}{6\pi i} \cdot [\, h_0^{(2)} \, \mathbf{P}(P') - \tfrac{1}{2} h_2^{(2)} \{ \mathbf{P}_{P'} - 3 (\mathbf{P}_{P'} \cdot \mathbf{r}^0) \, \mathbf{r}^0 \} \,]. \quad (18)$$

For the further calculation we may now choose for $\mathbf{P}$ a solution of (13), (14) representing a transverse plane wave propagated in an arbitrary direction: the result of the integration over all spatial orientations will in fact be independent of the choice of this direction. Let θ denote the angle between the direction $\mathbf{r}^0$ and the direction of propagation of the wave, and φ an azimuth in the plane of the wave. The azimuthal integration can be directly carried out upon $\mathsf{F} \cdot \mathbf{P}$ and yields

$$\int_0^{2\pi} d\varphi \, \mathsf{F}(P, P') \cdot \mathbf{P}(P') = - \tfrac{1}{3} i \sigma^3 \{ h_0^{(2)}(\zeta) - \tfrac{1}{2} P_2(\cos\theta) \, h_2^{(2)}(\zeta) \} \mathbf{P}(P');$$

moreover

$$\mathbf{P}(P') = \mathbf{P}(P) \exp (- i n \sigma r \cos\theta). \quad (19)$$

We thus see that the last integral in (12) reduces to a certain constant D times the polarization $\mathbf{P}$ at the point P. The expression for D may be obtained by expanding the exponential function

* It is convenient to observe that

$$\text{curl curl} = - \triangle + \text{grad div} = \sigma^2 + \text{grad div},$$

on account of (16).

which occurs in (19) in terms of Legendre polynomials (W 11.5–1):

$$\exp\left(-i\,\zeta'\cos\theta\right) = \sum_{m=0}^{\infty} (2m+1)\,i^m\,j_m(\zeta')\,P_m\left(\cos\theta\right),$$

with

$$\zeta' \equiv \sigma\,n\,r.$$

The integration over the angle θ in (18) can then be immediately effected by taking account of the orthogonality of the Legendre functions. The result is

$$D = -\tfrac{2}{3}\,i\,\sigma^3 \int\limits_{a}^{\infty} g(r)\,r^2\,dr\,\left\{ h_0^{(2)}(\sigma r)\,j_0(\sigma nr) + \tfrac{1}{2}\,h_2^{(2)}(\sigma r)\,j_2(\sigma nr) \right\}; \quad (20)$$

in this formula a represents the radius of the small sphere $s(P)$ surrounding the dipole at P.

Equation (12) may therefore be written in the simpler form

$$\mathbf{P}(P) = \gamma\,\Big\{ \mathbf{e}_0(P) + \int\limits_{s(P)}^{\Sigma} \mathsf{F}(P,P')\cdot\mathbf{P}(P')\,dv' \Big\}, \quad (21)$$

where the complex quantity γ is given by the formula

$$\gamma = N\left\{ \frac{1}{\gamma_a} + \frac{i}{6\pi}\left(\frac{\omega}{c}\right)^3 - D \right\}^{-1}, \quad (22)$$

generalizing (V, 32). This quantity γ represents the average polarizability of the medium, including the effects of radiation damping and density fluctuations. The expression between curly brackets on the right-hand side of (21) is then interpreted as the average field acting on the dipole at P when the spatial distribution of the molecules is treated as perfectly uniform. Putting for the average dipole field, according to (17),

$$\mathbf{E}_d \equiv \int\limits_{s(P)}^{\Sigma} \mathsf{F}(P,P')\cdot\mathbf{P}(P')\,dv' = \int\limits_{s(P)}^{\Sigma} \operatorname{curl\ curl}\ U\,\mathbf{P}(P')\,dv', \quad (23)$$

we may rewrite (21) as

$$\mathbf{P}(P) = \gamma\,\{\mathbf{e}_0(P) + \mathbf{E}_d(P)\}, \quad (24)$$

which, together with (23), brings out clearly the conclusions reached hitherto.

The occurrence of the constant D in (22) is a characteristic difference from, and an essential improvement upon, the elementary theory of the preceding chapter. We shall, however, postpone the discussion of the physical implications of formula (22) until we have established the desired connection between the polarizability γ and the parameter n.

3. THE TRANSVERSALITY CONDITION

To proceed further, it will be convenient to transform the dipole field (23) by bringing the differential operator curl curl outside the integral. It must be remembered that, in such a transfer of a differential operator, the small sphere $s(P)$ undergoes the same infinitesimal translation as its centre P, and this gives rise to an additional term in the form of a surface integral. In fact, for any partial derivative $\partial/\partial x$ and any function $F(P, P')$, one has

$$\frac{\partial}{\partial x} \int\limits_{s(P)}^{\Sigma} F(P, P')\, dv' = \int\limits_{s(P)}^{\Sigma} \frac{\partial F}{\partial x}\, dv' - \int\limits_{s(P)} F(P, P')\, r_x^0\, dS' \; ; \qquad (25)$$

$\mathbf{r}^0$ is, as above, the unit radial vector pointing outwards from P, and dS' is the element of surface of the small sphere. In evaluating such surface integrals we may, of course, retain only those quantities which do not vanish when the radius a of the sphere tends to zero.

In particular, if $F(P, P')$ is the product of the Green's function $U(P, P')$ by any function $G(P')$, the surface integral in (25) tends to zero as $a \to 0$. But a second derivation $\partial/\partial x$ gives rise to a finite surface integral

$$- \int\limits_{s(P)} G(P')\, \frac{\partial U}{\partial x}\, r_x^0\, dS' = - \int\limits_{s(P)} G(P')\, (r_x^0)^2\, \frac{dU}{dr}\, dS'$$

$$\to \frac{1}{4\pi}\, G(P) \int (r_x^0)^2\, d\Omega' = \tfrac{1}{3}\, G(P).$$

In this way one finds for the expression (23)

$$\mathbf{E}_d = \operatorname{curl} \operatorname{curl} \int\limits_{s(P)}^{\Sigma} U\, \mathbf{P}(P')\, dv' - \tfrac{2}{3}\, \mathbf{P}(P). \qquad (26)$$

Inserting this into (24), one obtains the fundamental integral equation in the new form

$$(1 + \tfrac{2}{3}\,\gamma)\,\mathbf{P}(P) = \gamma \left\{ \mathbf{e}_0(P) + \operatorname{curl} \operatorname{curl} \int\limits_{s(P)}^{\Sigma} U(P, P')\,\mathbf{P}(P')\,dv' \right\}. \quad (27)$$

Since div $\mathbf{e}_0 = 0$, it is immediately apparent that the condition (14) imposed upon $\mathbf{P}$ is compatible with this equation.

The condition (14) expresses the fact (of which use has already been made in Section 2) that the polarization of the medium is transverse to the direction of propagation of the transmitted wave. We shall eventually obtain the average field of the transmitted wave in terms of $\mathbf{P}$, and the transversality of $\mathbf{P}$ will then be seen to imply the same property for the transmitted wave.

4. THE EXTINCTION THEOREM

We have now to verify that our fundamental equation (27) can be satisfied by a polarization vector $\mathbf{P}$ propagated according to the wave equation (13), with a constant $n^2 \neq 1$. This seems at first sight surprising, since the field of the incident wave $\mathbf{e}_0$ occurring in (27) has the vacuum velocity of propagation c. We will now proceed to show, however, that if equations (13), (14) are assumed for $\mathbf{P}$ the contribution from the dipole field represented by the last term on the right-hand side of (27) can be decomposed into two parts, one of which obeys the wave equation *in vacuo* and exactly cancels the incident wave, while the other satisfies a wave equation of the type (13). The statement of this remarkable property constitutes the *extinction theorem* (in German *Auslöschungssatz*); the name recalls the fact that the incident wave is "extinguished" by interference with the dipole field and replaced by another wave with a different velocity of propagation.

The proof results from a simple application of Green's theorem:

$$\int\limits_{s(P)}^{\Sigma} (\mathbf{P}_{P'} \triangle_{P'} U - U \triangle_{P'} \mathbf{P}_{P'})\,dv'$$

$$= \int\limits_{\Sigma} (\mathbf{P}\,U_n - U\,\mathbf{P}_n)\,dS - \int\limits_{s(P)} \left(\mathbf{P}\,\frac{dU}{dr} - U\,\frac{\partial \mathbf{P}}{\partial r} \right) dS'; \quad (28)$$

in the first surface integral the index n denotes the normal derivative in the outward direction. From the left-hand side the Laplacians can be eliminated with the help of the wave equations (16) for U and (13) (as assumed) for $\mathbf{P}$: the left-hand side is thus reduced to

$$(n^2 - 1)\, \sigma^2 \int\limits_{s(P)}^{\Sigma} U\, \mathbf{P}_{P'}\, dv' \,.$$

The surface integral over the small sphere $s(P)$ on the right-hand side has the limiting value $-\mathbf{P}(P)$.

Applying now the operator curl curl to both sides, and observing that in virtue of (13) and (14), curl curl $\mathbf{P} = -\triangle \mathbf{P} = n^2 \sigma^2 \mathbf{P}$, we derive from (28) (provided that $n^2 \neq 1$)

$$\text{curl curl} \int\limits_{s(P)}^{\Sigma} U\, \mathbf{P}(P')\, dv'$$

$$= \frac{n^2}{n^2 - 1}\, \mathbf{P}(P) + \frac{1}{(n^2 - 1)\, \sigma^2}\, \text{curl curl} \int\limits_{\Sigma} (\mathbf{P}\, U_n - U\, \mathbf{P}_n)\, dS' . \qquad (29)$$

This formula exhibits the anticipated separation of the expression on the left-hand side into two parts which respectively satisfy the wave equations (13) and (16). Indeed, the first term on the right is assumed to obey (13), and it is obvious that the other term fulfils the vacuum wave equation (16). For the dipole field $\mathbf{E}_d$ itself, given by (26), we get a similar separation:

$$\mathbf{E}_d = \frac{n^2 + 2}{3\,(n^2 - 1)}\, \mathbf{P} + \frac{1}{(n^2 - 1)\, \sigma^2}\, \text{curl curl} \int\limits_{\Sigma} (\mathbf{P}\, U_n - U\, \mathbf{P}_n)\, dS' . \qquad (30)$$

Now, if we combine (29) with the fundamental equation (27), or more simply (30) with (24), we obtain an equality between two groups of terms each obeying a different wave equation: clearly, such an equality can only subsist if the two expressions vanish separately. This condition yields two distinct equations: the first,

$$\mathbf{e}_0 + \frac{1}{(n^2 - 1)\, \sigma^2}\, \text{curl curl} \int\limits_{\Sigma} (\mathbf{P}\, U_n - U\, \mathbf{P}_n)\, dS' = 0 \,, \qquad (31)$$

expresses the extinction of the incident wave by interference with a part of the dipole field; the second,

$$\frac{1}{\gamma} = \frac{n^2 + 2}{3(n^2 - 1)}, \tag{32}$$

establishes a relation between the polarizability γ and the parameter n, hitherto left undetermined.

The expression (31) for the extinction theorem shows that it is a contribution from the dipoles on the boundary of the medium which extinguishes the incident wave at any point inside. The polarization $\mathbf{P}$ is set up entirely by interactions between neighbouring dipoles: we can in fact picture the state of polarization of an unbounded medium as maintained by such neighbouring dipole interactions without taking the incident wave into consideration at all: the removal of the boundary of the medium to infinity causes no difficulty, since the only contribution from this boundary is just the extinction of the incident wave.

In order to complete the argument it only remains now to write down the expression for the average field $\mathbf{E}$ at any point taken at random in the medium. This field average differs from the field $\mathbf{e}_0 + \mathbf{E}_d$ acting on a dipole by the average value of the field produced at the centre of the small sphere $s(P)$ by a dipole situated at some point taken at random within that sphere. In other words, the additional field is that existing in the interior of a homogeneously polarized sphere, whose density of polarization is given by $N\mathbf{p}$, i.e. $\mathbf{P}$, since the average volume of a small sphere enclosing a dipole is N^{-1}. This field is just $-\frac{1}{3}\mathbf{P}$, as may be seen by an argument similar to that used in Chapter IV, Section 5, for the derivation of the internal field.

We have, therefore,

$$\mathbf{E} = \mathbf{e}_0 + \mathbf{E}_d - \tfrac{1}{3}\mathbf{P}. \tag{33}$$

This relation may be regarded as expressing the fact that the field $\mathbf{e}_0 + \mathbf{E}_d$ acting on a dipole is the sum of the average field $\mathbf{E}$ in the medium and an "internal field" $\frac{1}{3}\mathbf{P}$: but the latter quantity appears here under a rather different guise. Combined with the

expression (30) for the dipole field and (31) for the extinction
theorem, equation (33) gives

$$\mathbf{E} = \frac{1}{n^2 - 1}\, \mathbf{P}. \tag{34}$$

Equation (34) shows that $\mathbf{E}$ obeys the same wave equation as $\mathbf{P}$,
which establishes the physical meaning of the parameter n as the
complex refractive index of the medium. Moreover, $\mathbf{E}$ satisfies,
like $\mathbf{P}$, the transversality condition div $\mathbf{E} = 0$. For the average
electric displacement in the medium we have

$$\mathbf{D} = \mathbf{E} + \mathbf{P} = n^2 \mathbf{E}; \tag{35}$$

this provides the justification for the extrapolation of Maxwell's
relation (V, 14) on which the elementary dispersion theory is
based. Alternatively, we may say that the interpretation of n
as refractive index entails a physical interpretation of our derivation
of equation (32) connecting the parameter n with the polarizability
γ of the medium: this derivation becomes a proof of the Lorentz–
Lorenz relation (which, in the elementary theory, was simply
extrapolated from the limiting case of very low frequencies).
Finally, it should be observed that equation (34) has been used,
in the form of (V, 35), in the direct calculation of the scattering
coefficient: this calculation, too, is thus put on a firm basis.

5. THE EXTINCTION COEFFICIENT

Our expression (22) for the polarizability of the medium may be
combined with the Lorentz–Lorenz relation (32), as in Chapter V,
Section 4, to yield a theory of refractive index and extinction
coefficient applicable to any physical state of the medium. The
influence of molecular distribution is in fact embodied in the
constant D, defined by (20), and it is of special interest to compare
the general expression for the extinction coefficient which we are
now able to derive, with the results of the direct discussion of the
scattering phenomenon, carried out in the two last sections of
the preceding chapter.

In the expression (20) for the constant D we may of course disregard the imaginary part of the refractive index. The substitution

$$h_0^{(2)} = j_0 + i\,j_{-1}\,, \quad h_2^{(2)} = j_2 + i\,j_{-3}$$

then directly gives the decomposition of D into its real and imaginary part. The real part of D, as formula (22) shows, will give rise to a slight modification of the inverse polarizability γ_a^{-1}; if this quantity reduces to a single predominant term $(e_k^2/m_k)^{-1}(\omega_k^2 - \omega^2)$, this modification may be described as a shift of the resonance frequency ω_k, which is usually quite insignificant; in fact, the order of magnitude of the relative frequency shift, for small values of the correlation range ($\varkappa\sigma \ll 1$) is easily found to be *

$$\frac{e_k^2/m_k\,c^2}{\varkappa}\,G,$$

where G is the space integral of the correlation function (V, 47). We shall not discuss this effect further.

The imaginary term of D, on the other hand, has the remarkable form $-\,i(6\pi)^{-1}\sigma^3 G_\varphi$, where G_φ is the characteristic quantity occurring in the theory of scattering and defined by the general formula (V, 67). It combines with the radiation damping term to give rise, in the expression (22), to a total dissipative contribution $i(6\pi)^{-1}\sigma^3(1 + G_\varphi)$. The resulting expression for the extinction coefficient is

$$a' = a\,(1 + G_\varphi), \tag{36}$$

where a is given by the Rayleigh formula (V, 33). This generalization of Rayleigh's formula is, as expected, in full agreement with the expression (V, 60) for the scattering coefficient of a non-ideal gas. The equivalence of the two points of view — dissipative forces on the dipoles on the one hand, scattering of the incident radiation on the other — is thus established for the whole range of validity of Ornstein and Zernike's theory.

Moreover, as explained above, we may regard the derivation of formula (36) as valid also for perfect crystals, in the domain of

---

*   For small values of ζ one finds

$$j_{-1}(\zeta)\,j_0(n\zeta) + \tfrac{1}{2}\,j_{-3}(\zeta)\,j_2(n\zeta) \approx \frac{1}{\zeta}\left(1 + \frac{n^2}{10}\right).$$

large wave-lengths here considered, provided that the correlation function $g(r)$ is given the proper form. For sufficiently small σ we have $G_\varphi \approx G$, and the relation $1 + G = 0$, expressing the absence of density fluctuations in the crystal, implies also the absence of extinction (and scattering) of light.

While these results form the exact counterpart of the situation met with in the investigation of the scattering of the incident radiation, they illustrate the phenomenon from a different aspect. Thus, we see that in a gas of low density, when $G_\varphi \approx 0$, the energy dissipation of the dipoles is due to radiation damping only (as was assumed without proof in the elementary theory of Chapter V). In the opposite extreme case of a crystal there is no dissipation of energy: the energy lost by a dipole as a result of the emission of radiation is regenerated by the coherent action of the radiation coming from the other dipoles.

APPENDIX

ON TENSOR NOTATION

The representation of tensors by their components, distinguished by a set of indices, has the advantage of complete generality with regard both to the number of dimensions of the space in which the tensors operate and to the rank of the tensors. When dealing only with vectors and their linear transformations, however, it is often convenient to use a "shorthand" notation in which the emphasis is put on the geometrical or physical significance of the vectors and tensors rather than on the sets of components necessary for their quantitative evaluation. In this system of notation, different letter-types are used to denote the successive ranks of tensors: italics for scalars, Clarendon for vectors, sanserif for tensors (of the second rank). Thus — denoting by an arrow the equivalence between a symbolic expression and a set of expressions involving tensor components — we write

$$\mathbf{a} \to a_i$$
$$\mathsf{T} \to T_{ik}.$$

1. EXTERIOR PRODUCT; DYAD

The *exterior product* of two tensors of any ranks n, n' is the tensor of rank $n + n'$ formed by multiplication of the components of the two tensors in a definite order. It will be denoted by simple juxtaposition of the symbols representing the tensors. Thus,

$$\mathbf{a}\mathsf{T} \to (\mathbf{a}\mathsf{T})_{ikl} = a_i T_{kl}$$
$$\mathsf{T}\mathbf{a} \to (\mathsf{T}\mathbf{a})_{ikl} = T_{ik} a_l.$$

The exterior product of an ordered pair of vectors $\mathbf{a}$, $\mathbf{b}$ is a tensor

$$\mathsf{D} = \mathbf{a}\mathbf{b} \to D_{ik} = a_i b_k,$$

called by Gibbs a *dyad*.

2. CONTRACTION; INTERIOR PRODUCT

The rank of any tensor may be lowered by two units by the operation called *contraction*. This consists in putting equal two indices and performing a summation over the resulting "dummy" index. Thus, one way of contracting the tensor T_{ikl} is to put $k = l$ and to form

$$\sum_l T_{ill};$$

the result in this case is a vector. The contraction of a tensor of the second rank T_{ik} yields the scalar $\sum_i T_{ii}$, called the *trace* of the tensor.

The *interior product* of two tensors is derived from the exterior product by contracting the latter with respect to the neighbouring indices belonging to each of the tensors respectively. In our symbolical notation, the interior product is indicated by inserting a dot between the symbols of the tensors. Thus, we may form the interior product of two vectors **a**, **b**, usually called their *scalar product*,

$$\mathbf{a} \cdot \mathbf{b} = \sum_i a_i b_i,$$

and the interior product of two tensors (of the second rank)

$$\mathsf{S} \cdot \mathsf{T} \quad \rightarrow \quad (\mathsf{S} \cdot \mathsf{T})_{ik} = \sum_l S_{il} T_{lk}.$$

In the latter case, a further contraction gives the trace of the tensor $\mathsf{S} \cdot \mathsf{T}$; this may conveniently be denoted by inserting another dot between the symbols, thus:

$$\mathsf{S} : \mathsf{T} = \sum_{i,l} S_{il} T_{li}.$$

The successive dots may be taken to indicate contractions with respect to the nearest distinct indices on each side of the dot. For a tensor T and a vector **u**, we have the interior products

$$\mathsf{T} \cdot \mathbf{u} \quad \rightarrow \quad (\mathsf{T} \cdot \mathbf{u})_i = \sum_k T_{ik} u_k$$

$$\mathbf{u} \cdot \mathsf{T} \quad \rightarrow \quad (\mathbf{u} \cdot \mathsf{T})_i = \sum_k u_k T_{ki},$$

which show how a tensor "operates" on a vector, either "on the left" or "on the right", transforming this vector into another one.

The operation of the dyad $D = ab$ is expressed by the formulae

$$D \cdot u = a\,(b \cdot u), \qquad u \cdot D = (u \cdot a)\,b.$$

The notions of exterior and interior products, and the corresponding symbolic notation, can of course be extended to more than two tensors. Thus, the reader will easily interpret the expression $u \cdot T \cdot v$ and check the identity

$$u \cdot T \cdot v = v\,u : T.$$

3. SYMMETRY AND ANTISYMMETRY

The tensor derived from a given tensor T by transposing the indices is called the *conjugate* of T and denoted by T_C:

$$T_{C,ik} = T_{ki}.$$

This definition may be expressed by the relation

$$T_C \cdot u = u \cdot T,$$

valid identically for any vector u.

From the tensor T and its conjugate T_C we construct the *symmetrical* (self-conjugate) tensor

$$T_S = \tfrac{1}{2}\,(T + T_C) \quad \rightarrow \quad T_{S,ik} = \tfrac{1}{2}\,(T_{ik} + T_{ki}) = T_{S,ki}$$

and the *antisymmetrical* tensor

$$T_A = \tfrac{1}{2}\,(T - T_C) \quad \rightarrow \quad T_{A,ik} = \tfrac{1}{2}\,(T_{ik} - T_{ki}) = -T_{A,ki}.$$

In this way, the tensor T is decomposed into a symmetrical and an antisymmetrical part:

$$T = T_S + T_A.$$

The conjugate of the dyad $D = ab$ is the dyad $D_C = ba$. We may therefore write

$$D = D_S + D_A,$$

with

$$D_S = \tfrac{1}{2}\,(ab + ba) \quad \rightarrow \quad D_{S,ik} = \tfrac{1}{2}\,(a_i\,b_k + a_k\,b_i)$$
$$D_A = \tfrac{1}{2}\,(ab - ba) \quad \rightarrow \quad D_{A,ik} = \tfrac{1}{2}\,(a_i\,b_k - a_k\,b_i).$$

In the case of ordinary three-dimensional space, the antisymmetrical part of the dyad **ab** is connected with the *vector product* of the two vectors

$$\mathbf{a} \wedge \mathbf{b} \quad \rightarrow \quad (\mathbf{a} \wedge \mathbf{b})_x = a_y b_z - a_z b_y, \ldots$$

by the easily verified relations, valid for any vector **u**,

$$\mathsf{D}_A \cdot \mathbf{u} = -\tfrac{1}{2}(\mathbf{a} \wedge \mathbf{b}) \wedge \mathbf{u}, \qquad \mathbf{u} \cdot \mathsf{D}_A = -\tfrac{1}{2}\mathbf{u} \wedge (\mathbf{a} \wedge \mathbf{b}).$$

For any two tensors T, V one has obviously

$$\mathsf{T} : \mathsf{V} = \mathsf{T}_S : \mathsf{V}_S + \mathsf{T}_A : \mathsf{V}_A;$$

in each term on the right-hand side, one of the indices S or A may be omitted, if convenient. For two dyads $\mathsf{D} = \mathbf{ab}$, $\mathsf{D}' = \mathbf{a'b'}$, it is readily found that

$$\mathsf{D}_A : \mathsf{D}'_A = -\tfrac{1}{2}(\mathbf{a} \wedge \mathbf{b}) \cdot (\mathbf{a'} \wedge \mathbf{b'}).$$

4. SPATIAL DERIVATION

The operator of spatial derivation may be treated as a symbolical vector

$$\mathit{\nabla} \rightarrow \frac{\partial}{\partial x_i}.$$

By exterior multiplication of $\mathit{\nabla}$ with a scalar or a vector we define the *gradients* of these quantities:

$$\operatorname{grad} m = \mathit{\nabla} m \quad \rightarrow \quad (\operatorname{grad} m)_i = \frac{\partial m}{\partial x_i},$$

$$\operatorname{Grad} \mathbf{a} = \mathit{\nabla} \mathbf{a} \quad \rightarrow \quad (\operatorname{Grad} \mathbf{a})_{ik} = \frac{\partial a_k}{\partial x_i};$$

the former is a vector, the latter a dyad. The interior products of $\mathit{\nabla}$ with a vector or a tensor define the corresponding *divergences*:

$$\operatorname{div} \mathbf{a} = \mathit{\nabla} \cdot \mathbf{a} \quad \rightarrow \quad \operatorname{div} \mathbf{a} = \sum_i \frac{\partial a_i}{\partial x_i},$$

$$\operatorname{Div} \mathsf{T} = \mathit{\nabla} \cdot \mathsf{T} \quad \rightarrow \quad (\operatorname{Div} \mathsf{T})_k = \sum_i \frac{\partial T_{ik}}{\partial x_i},$$

which are a scalar and a vector, respectively.

The gradient of a vector may be decomposed into a symmetrical and an antisymmetrical part:

$$\text{Grad } \mathbf{a} = (\text{Grad } \mathbf{a})_S + (\text{Grad } \mathbf{a})_A,$$

with

$$(\text{Grad } \mathbf{a})_{S,ik} = \tfrac{1}{2} \left(\frac{\partial a_k}{\partial x_i} + \frac{\partial a_i}{\partial x_k} \right)$$

$$(\text{Grad } \mathbf{a})_{A,ik} = \tfrac{1}{2} \left(\frac{\partial a_k}{\partial x_i} - \frac{\partial a_i}{\partial x_k} \right).$$

The latter tensor, in ordinary space, is related to the *curl* of the vector **a**

$$\text{curl } \mathbf{a} = \nabla \wedge \mathbf{a} \quad \rightarrow \quad (\text{curl } \mathbf{a})_x = \frac{\partial a_z}{\partial y} - \frac{\partial a_y}{\partial z}, \ldots$$

by either of the formulae

$$(\text{Grad } \mathbf{a})_A \cdot \mathbf{u} = -\tfrac{1}{2} (\text{curl } \mathbf{a}) \wedge \mathbf{u}$$

$$\mathbf{u} \cdot (\text{Grad } \mathbf{a})_A = -\tfrac{1}{2} \mathbf{u} \wedge \text{curl } \mathbf{a},$$

valid for any vector **u**.

As an example of symbolic tensor calculus, using some of the preceding formulae, the reader may derive the relation

$$\mathbf{u} \cdot \text{Grad } \mathbf{a} \cdot \mathbf{v} = \mathbf{v}\mathbf{u} : \text{Grad } \mathbf{a}$$

$$= \tfrac{1}{2} (\mathbf{v}\mathbf{u} + \mathbf{u}\mathbf{v}) : \text{Grad } \mathbf{a} - \tfrac{1}{2} (\mathbf{v} \wedge \mathbf{u}) \cdot \text{curl } \mathbf{a}.$$

Applied to the evaluation of the expression (III, 10), this relation provides an alternative derivation of the formulae (III, 12) and (III, 13), more elegant than that given in the text.

Note. The system of tensor notation here outlined is essentially that of Milne and Chapman, fully described in S. Chapman and T. Cowling's book *The mathematical theory of non-uniform gases* (Cambridge 1939).

INDEX

absorption 64, 68ff, resonance 70,
see also extinction, scattering
absorption line, width 69, 70
addition theorem of Bessel functions 87
additivity of polarizability 65
Andant, A. 89
Andrews, T. 86
angular momentum 37ff, 44
anomalous dispersion 68, 70, Zeeman effect 37, 38
antisymmetry of tensor 113
Arago, D. F. 79
Auslöschungssatz 94, 105
averages over physically infinitesimal regions 15, of field intensities 17
barium titanate 63
Barkhausen effect 56
Barnett, S. J. 39, 40
Barnett effect 39, 43
Bates, L. 44
bees 79
Bessel functions, spherical 85, 87, addition theorem 87
birefringence 92
blue colour of sky 74
Bohr, N. 47
Bohr magneton 51
Bozorth, R. 56
Busch G. 64,
cathode rays 2ff
charge, elementary 8, specific 5, conservation 15
charge density, average 17ff, free 17, 20, 22, true 17, 22
classical theory of magnetism, paradox of 46

coercitivity 56
collision damping 71, 73
Compton effect 80
conduction in electrolytes 1, in gases 2
conduction current 23
conjugate tensor 113
conservation of charge 15
contraction of tensor 112
Coriolis force 35
correlation function 82, 84, 85, direct 82, 83, differential equation 84, integral equation 83
correlation integral 82ff
correlation range 82, 85, 86, 89
critical opalescence 80ff
critical point, scattering at 87, 89, 90
critical temperature 86, 87, 89, 90, see also Curie point
crystal, scattering by 78, 97, 109
Curie, M. 7
Curie, P. 7, 51
Curie law 50, 51, 62
Curie point 53, 54, 58, 63
Curie–Weiss law 55, 58, 63
current, inertia of 41, types of 23
current density, average 22ff
damping 68, 71, collision 71, 73, radiative 71, 93, 109
Debye, P. 61, 62
Debye's theory of polarizability 61, 62
density fluctuations 81ff
diamagnetic susceptibility 45, 46
diamagnetism 45
dichroism 92

CATALOGUE OF DOVER BOOKS

PHYSICS

General physics

FOUNDATIONS OF PHYSICS, R. B. Lindsay & H. Margenau. Excellent bridge between semi-popular works & technical treatises. A discussion of methods of physical description, construction of theory; valuable for physicist with elementary calculus who is interested in ideas that give meaning to data, tools of modern physics. Contents include symbolism, mathematical equations; space & time foundations of mechanics; probability; physics & continua; electron theory; special & general relativity; quantum mechanics; causality. "Thorough and yet not overdetailed. Unreservedly recommended," NATURE (London). Unabridged, corrected edition. List of recommended readings. 35 illustrations. xi + 537pp. 5⅜ x 8.
S377 Paperbound **$2.75**

FUNDAMENTAL FORMULAS OF PHYSICS, ed. by D. H. Menzel. Highly useful, fully inexpensive reference and study text, ranging from simple to highly sophisticated operations. Mathematics integrated into text—each chapter stands as short textbook of field represented. Vol. 1: Statistics, Physical Constants, Special Theory of Relativity, Hydrodynamics, Aerodynamics, Boundary Value Problems in Math. Physics; Viscosity, Electromagnetic Theory, etc. Vol. 2: Sound, Acoustics, Geometrical Optics, Electron Optics, High-Energy Phenomena, Magnetism, Biophysics, much more. Index. Total of 800pp. 5⅜ x 8.
Vol. 1 S595 Paperbound **$2.00**
Vol. 2 S596 Paperbound **$2.00**

MATHEMATICAL PHYSICS, D. H. Menzel. Thorough one-volume treatment of the mathematical techniques vital for classic mechanics, electromagnetic theory, quantum theory, and relativity. Written by the Harvard Professor of Astrophysics for junior, senior, and graduate courses, it gives clear explanations of all those aspects of function theory, vectors, matrices, dyadics, tensors, partial differential equations, etc., necessary for the understanding of the various physical theories. Electron theory, relativity, and other topics seldom presented appear here in considerable detail. Scores of definitions, conversion factors, dimensional constants, etc. "More detailed than normal for an advanced text . . . excellent set of sections on Dyadics, Matrices, and Tensors," JOURNAL OF THE FRANKLIN INSTITUTE. Index. 193 problems, with answers. x + 412pp. 5⅜ x 8.
S56 Paperbound **$2.00**

THE SCIENTIFIC PAPERS OF J. WILLARD GIBBS. All the published papers of America's outstanding theoretical scientist (except for "Statistical Mechanics" and "Vector Analysis"). Vol I (thermodynamics) contains one of the most brilliant of all 19th-century scientific papers—the 300-page "On the Equilibrium of Heterogeneous Substances," which founded the science of physical chemistry, and clearly stated a number of highly important natural laws for the first time; 8 other papers complete the first volume. Vol II includes 2 papers on dynamics, 8 on vector analysis and multiple algebra, 5 on the electromagnetic theory of light, and 6 miscellaneous papers. Biographical sketch by H. A. Bumstead. Total of xxxvi + 718pp. 5⅝ x 8⅜.
S721 Vol I Paperbound **$2.50**
S722 Vol II Paperbound **$2.00**
The set **$4.50**

BASIC THEORIES OF PHYSICS, Peter Gabriel Bergmann. Two-volume set which presents a critical examination of important topics in the major subdivisions of classical and modern physics. The first volume is concerned with classical mechanics and electrodynamics: mechanics of mass points, analytical mechanics, matter in bulk, electrostatics and magnetostatics, electromagnetic interaction, the field waves, special relativity, and waves. The second volume (Heat and Quanta) contains discussions of the kinetic hypothesis, physics and statistics, stationary ensembles, laws of thermodynamics, early quantum theories, atomic spectra, probability waves, quantization in wave mechanics, approximation methods, and abstract quantum theory. A valuable supplement to any thorough course or text.
Heat and Quanta: Index. 8 figures. x + 300pp. 5⅜ x 8½.　　S968 Paperbound **$1.75**
Mechanics and Electrodynamics: Index. 14 figures. vii + 280pp. 5⅜ x 8½.
S969 Paperbound **$1.75**

THEORETICAL PHYSICS, A. S. Kompaneyets. One of the very few thorough studies of the subject in this price range. Provides advanced students with a comprehensive theoretical background. Especially strong on recent experimentation and developments in quantum theory. Contents: Mechanics (Generalized Coordinates, Lagrange's Equation, Collision of Particles, etc.), Electrodynamics (Vector Analysis, Maxwell's equations, Transmission of Signals, Theory of Relativity, etc.), Quantum Mechanics (the Inadequacy of Classical Mechanics, the Wave Equation, Motion in a Central Field, Quantum Theory of Radiation, Quantum Theories of Dispersion and Scattering, etc.), and Statistical Physics (Equilibrium Distribution of Molecules in an Ideal Gas, Boltzmann statistics, Bose and Fermi Distribution, Thermodynamic Quantities, etc.). Revised to 1961. Translated by George Yankovsky, authorized by Kompaneyets. 137 exercises. 56 figures. 529pp. 5⅜ x 8½. S972 Paperbound **$2.50**

ANALYTICAL AND CANONICAL FORMALISM IN PHYSICS, André Mercier. A survey, in one volume, of the variational principles (the key principles—in mathematical form—from which the basic laws of any one branch of physics can be derived) of the several branches of physical theory, together with an examination of the relationships among them. Contents: the Lagrangian Formalism, Lagrangian Densities, Canonical Formalism, Canonical Form of Electrodynamics, Hamiltonian Densities, Transformations, and Canonical Form with Vanishing Jacobian Determinant. Numerous examples and exercises. For advanced students, teachers, etc. 6 figures. Index. viii + 222pp. 5⅜ x 8½.　　S1077 Paperbound **$1.75**

Acoustics, optics, electricity and magnetism, electromagnetics, magneto-hydrodynamics

THE THEORY OF SOUND, Lord Rayleigh. Most vibrating systems likely to be encountered in practice can be tackled successfully by the methods set forth by the great Nobel laureate, Lord Rayleigh. Complete coverage of experimental, mathematical aspects of sound theory. Partial contents: Harmonic motions, vibrating systems in general, lateral vibrations of bars, curved plates or shells, applications of Laplace's functions to acoustical problems, fluid friction, plane vortex-sheet, vibrations of solid bodies, etc. This is the first inexpensive edition of this great reference and study work. Bibliography. Historical introduction by R. B. Lindsay. Total of 1040pp. 97 figures. 5⅜ x 8.
S292, S293, Two volume set, paperbound, **$4.70**

THE DYNAMICAL THEORY OF SOUND, H. Lamb. Comprehensive mathematical treatment of the physical aspects of sound, covering the theory of vibrations, the general theory of sound, and the equations of motion of strings, bars, membranes, pipes, and resonators. Includes chapters on plane, spherical, and simple harmonic waves, and the Helmholtz Theory of Audition. Complete and self-contained development for student and specialist; all fundamental differential equations solved completely. Specific mathematical details for such important phenomena as harmonics, normal modes, forced vibrations of strings, theory of reed pipes, etc. Index. Bibliography. 86 diagrams. viii + 307pp. 5⅜ x 8.
S655 Paperbound **$1.50**

WAVE PROPAGATION IN PERIODIC STRUCTURES, L. Brillouin. A general method and application to different problems: pure physics, such as scattering of X-rays of crystals, thermal vibration in crystal lattices, electronic motion in metals; and also problems of electrical engineering. Partial contents: elastic waves in 1-dimensional lattices of point masses. Propagation of waves along 1-dimensional lattices. Energy flow. 2 dimensional, 3 dimensional lattices. Mathieu's equation. Matrices and propagation of waves along an electric line. Continuous electric lines. 131 illustrations. Bibliography. Index. xii + 253pp. 5⅜ x 8.
S34 Paperbound **$2.00**

THEORY OF VIBRATIONS, N. W. McLachlan. Based on an exceptionally successful graduate course given at Brown University, this discusses linear systems having 1 degree of freedom, forced vibrations of simple linear systems, vibration of flexible strings, transverse vibrations of bars and tubes, transverse vibration of circular plate, sound waves of finite amplitude, etc. Index. 99 diagrams. 160pp. 5⅜ x 8.
S190 Paperbound **$1.35**

LIGHT: PRINCIPLES AND EXPERIMENTS, George S. Monk. Covers theory, experimentation, and research. Intended for students with some background in general physics and elementary calculus. Three main divisions: 1) Eight chapters on geometrical optics—fundamental concepts (the ray and its optical length, Fermat's principle, etc.), laws of image formation, apertures in optical systems, photometry, optical instruments etc.; 2) 9 chapters on physical optics—interference, diffraction, polarization, spectra, the Rayleigh refractometer, the wave theory of light, etc.; 3) 23 instructive experiments based directly on the theoretical text. "Probably the best intermediate textbook on light in the English language. Certainly, it is the best book which includes both geometrical and physical optics," J. Rud Nielson, PHYSICS FORUM. Revised edition. 102 problems and answers. 12 appendices. 6 tables. Index. 270 illustrations. xi +489pp. 5⅜ x 8½.
S341 Paperbound **$2.50**

PHOTOMETRY, John W. T. Walsh. The best treatment of both "bench" and "illumination" photometry in English by one of Britain's foremost experts in the field (President of the International Commission on Illumination). Limited to those matters, theoretical and practical, which affect the measurement of light flux, candlepower, illumination, etc., and excludes treatment of the use to which such measurements may be put after they have been made. Chapters on Radiation, The Eye and Vision, Photo-Electric Cells, The Principles of Photometry, The Measurement of Luminous Intensity, Colorimetry, Spectrophotometry, Stellar Photometry, The Photometric Laboratory, etc. Third revised (1958) edition. 281 illustrations. 10 appendices. xxiv + 544pp. 5½ x 9¼.
S319 Clothbound **$10.00**

EXPERIMENTAL SPECTROSCOPY, R. A. Sawyer. Clear discussion of prism and grating spectrographs and the techniques of their use in research, with emphasis on those principles and techniques that are fundamental to practically all uses of spectroscopic equipment. Beginning with a brief history of spectroscopy, the author covers such topics as light sources, spectroscopic apparatus, prism spectroscopes and graphs, diffraction grating, the photographic process, determination of wave length, spectral intensity, infrared spectroscopy, spectrochemical analysis, etc. This revised edition contains new material on the production of replica gratings, solar spectroscopy from rockets, new standard of wave length, etc. Index. Bibliography. 111 illustrations. x + 358pp. 5⅜ x 8½.
S1045 Paperbound **$2.25**

FUNDAMENTALS OF ELECTRICITY AND MAGNETISM, L. B. Loeb. For students of physics, chemistry, or engineering who want an introduction to electricity and magnetism on a higher level and in more detail than general elementary physics texts provide. Only elementary differential and integral calculus is assumed. Physical laws developed logically, from magnetism to electric currents, Ohm's law, electrolysis, and on to static electricity, induction, etc. Covers an unusual amount of material; one third of book on modern material: solution of wave equation, photoelectric and thermionic effects, etc. Complete statement of the various electrical systems of units and interrelations. 2 Indexes. 75 pages of problems with answers stated. Over 300 figures and diagrams. xix +669pp. 5⅜ x 8.
S745 Paperbound **$2.75**

MATHEMATICAL ANALYSIS OF ELECTRICAL AND OPTICAL WAVE-MOTION, Harry Bateman. Written by one of this century's most distinguished mathematical physicists, this is a practical introduction to those developments of Maxwell's electromagnetic theory which are directly connected with the solution of the partial differential equation of wave motion. Methods of solving wave-equation, polar-cylindrical coordinates, diffraction, transformation of coordinates, homogeneous solutions, electromagnetic fields with moving singularities, etc. Index. 168pp. 5⅜ x 8. S14 Paperbound **$1.75**

PRINCIPLES OF PHYSICAL OPTICS, Ernst Mach. This classical examination of the propagation of light, color, polarization, etc. offers an historical and philosophical treatment that has never been surpassed for breadth and easy readability. Contents: Rectilinear propagation of light. Reflection, refraction. Early knowledge of vision. Dioptrics. Composition of light. Theory of color and dispersion. Periodicity. Theory of interference. Polarization. Mathematical representation of properties of light. Propagation of waves, etc. 279 illustrations, 10 portraits. Appendix. Indexes. 324pp. 5⅜ x 8. S178 Paperbound **$2.00**

THE THEORY OF OPTICS, Paul Drude. One of finest fundamental texts in physical optics, classic offers thorough coverage, complete mathematical treatment of basic ideas. Includes fullest treatment of application of thermodynamics to optics; sine law in formation of images, transparent crystals, magnetically active substances, velocity of light, apertures, effects depending upon them, polarization, optical instruments, etc. Introduction by A. A. Michelson. Index. 110 illus. 567pp. 5⅜ x 8. S532 Paperbound **$2.45**

ELECTRICAL THEORY ON THE GIORGI SYSTEM, P. Cornelius. A new clarification of the fundamental concepts of electricity and magnetism, advocating the convenient m.k.s. system of units that is steadily gaining followers in the sciences. Illustrating the use and effectiveness of his terminology with numerous applications to concrete technical problems, the author here expounds the famous Giorgi system of electrical physics. His lucid presentation and well-reasoned, cogent argument for the universal adoption of this system form one of the finest pieces of scientific exposition in recent years. 28 figures. Index. Conversion tables for translating earlier data into modern units. Translated from 3rd Dutch edition by L. J. Jolley. x + 187pp. 5½ x 8¾. S909 Clothbound **$6.00**

ELECTRIC WAVES: BEING RESEARCHES ON THE PROPAGATION OF ELECTRIC ACTION WITH FINITE VELOCITY THROUGH SPACE, Heinrich Hertz. This classic work brings together the original papers in which Hertz—Helmholtz's protegé and one of the most brilliant figures in 19th-century research—probed the existence of electromagnetic waves and showed experimentally that their velocity equalled that of light, research that helped lay the groundwork for the development of radio, television, telephone, telegraph, and other modern technological marvels. Unabridged republication of original edition. Authorized translation by D. E. Jones. Preface by Lord Kelvin. Index of names. 40 illustrations. xvii + 278pp. 5⅜ x 8½. S57 Paperbound **$1.75**

PIEZOELECTRICITY: AN INTRODUCTION TO THE THEORY AND APPLICATIONS OF ELECTRO-MECHANICAL PHENOMENA IN CRYSTALS, Walter G. Cady. This is the most complete and systematic coverage of this important field in print—now regarded as something of scientific classic. This republication, revised and corrected by Prof. Cady—one of the foremost contributors in this area—contains a sketch of recent progress and new material on Ferroelectrics. Time Standards, etc. The first 7 chapters deal with fundamental theory of crystal electricity. 5 important chapters cover basic concepts of piezoelectricity, including comparisons of various competing theories in the field. Also discussed: piezoelectric resonators (theory, methods of manufacture, influences of air-gaps, etc.); the piezo oscillator; the properties, history, and observations relating to Rochelle salt; ferroelectric crystals; miscellaneous applications of piezoelectricity; pyroelectricity; etc. "A great work," W. A. Wooster, NATURE. Revised (1963) and corrected edition. New preface by Prof. Cady. 2 Appendices. Indices. Illustrations. 62 tables. Bibliography. Problems. Total of 1 + 822pp. 5⅜ x 8½.
S1094 Vol. I Paperbound **$2.50**
S1095 Vol. II Paperbound **$2.50**
Two volume set Paperbound **$5.00**

MAGNETISM AND VERY LOW TEMPERATURES, H. B. G. Casimir. A basic work in the literature of low temperature physics. Presents a concise survey of fundamental theoretical principles, and also points out promising lines of investigation. Contents: Classical Theory and Experimental Methods, Quantum Theory of Paramagnetism, Experiments on Adiabatic Demagnetization. Theoretical Discussion of Paramagnetism at Very Low Temperatures, Some Experimental Results, Relaxation Phenomena. Index. 89-item bibliography. ix + 95pp. 5⅜ x 8. S943 Paperbound **$1.25**

SELECTED PAPERS ON NEW TECHNIQUES FOR ENERGY CONVERSION: THERMOELECTRIC METHODS; THERMIONIC; PHOTOVOLTAIC AND ELECTRICAL EFFECTS; FUSION, Edited by Sumner N. Levine. Brings together in one volume the most important papers (1954-1961) in modern energy technology. Included among the 37 papers are general and qualitative descriptions of the field as a whole, indicating promising lines of research. Also: 15 papers on thermoelectric methods, 7 on thermionic, 5 on photovoltaic, 4 on electrochemical effect, and 2 on controlled fusion research. Among the contributors are: Joffe, Maria Telkes, Herold, Herring, Douglas, Jaumot; Post, Austin, Wilson, Pfann, Rappaport, Morehouse, Domenicali, Moss, Bowers, Harman, Von Doenhoef. Preface and introduction by the editor. Bibliographies. xxviii + 451pp. 6⅛ x 9¼. S37 Paperbound **$3.00**

SUPERFLUIDS: MACROSCOPIC THEORY OF SUPERCONDUCTIVITY, Vol. I, Fritz London. The major work by one of the founders and great theoreticians of modern quantum physics. Consolidates the researches that led to the present understanding of the nature of super-conductivity. Prof. London here reveals that quantum mechanics is operative on the macro-scopic plane as well as the submolecular level. Contents: Properties of Superconductors and Their Thermodynamical Correlation; Electrodynamics of the Pure Superconducting State; Relation between Current and Field; Measurements of the Penetration Depth; Non-Viscous Flow vs. Superconductivity; Micro-waves in Superconductors; Reality of the Domain Structure; and many other related topics. A new epilogue by M. J. Buckingham discusses developments in the field up to 1960. Corrected and expanded edition. An appreciation of the author's life and work by L. W. Nordheim. Biography by Edith London. Bibliography of his publica-tions. 45 figures. 2 Indices. xviii + 173pp. 5⅜ x 8⅜.   S44 Paperbound **$1.45**

SELECTED PAPERS ON PHYSICAL PROCESSES IN IONIZED PLASMAS, Edited by Donald H. Menzel, Director, Harvard College Observatory. 30 important papers relating to the study of highly ionized gases or plasmas selected by a foremost contributor in the field,' with the assistance of Dr. L. H. Aller. The essays include 18 on the physical processes in gaseous nebulae, covering problems of radiation and radiative transfer, the Balmer decrement, electron temperatures, spectrophotometry, etc. 10 papers deal with the interpretation of nebular spectra, by Bohm, Van Vleck, Aller, Minkowski, etc. There is also a discussion of the intensities of "forbidden" spectral lines by George Shortley and a paper concern-ing the theory of hydrogenic spectra by Menzel and Pekeris. Other contributors: Goldberg, Hebb, Baker, Bowen, Ufford, Liller, etc. viii + 374pp. 6⅛ x 9¼.   S60 Paperbound **$2.95**

THE ELECTROMAGNETIC FIELD, Max Mason & Warren Weaver. Used constantly by graduate engineers. Vector methods exclusively: detailed treatment of electrostatics, expansion meth-ods, with tables converting any quantity into absolute electromagnetic, absolute electrostatic, practical units. Discrete charges, ponderable bodies, Maxwell field equations, etc. Introduc-tion. Indexes. 416pp. 5⅜ x 8.   S185 Paperbound **$2.00**

THEORY OF ELECTRONS AND ITS APPLICATION TO THE PHENOMENA OF LIGHT AND RADIANT HEAT, H. Lorentz. Lectures delivered at Columbia University by Nobel laureate Lorentz. Unabridged, they form a historical coverage of the theory of free electrons, motion, absorption of heat, Zeeman effect, propagation of light in molecular bodies, inverse Zeeman effect, optical phenomena in moving bodies, etc. 109 pages of notes explain the more advanced sections. Index. 9 figures. 352pp. 5⅜ x 8.   S173 Paperbound **$1.85**

FUNDAMENTAL ELECTROMAGNETIC THEORY, Ronold P. King, Professor Applied Physics, Harvard University. Original and valuable introduction to electromagnetic theory and to circuit theory from the standpoint of electromagnetic theory. Contents: Mathematical Description of Matter—stationary and nonstationary states; Mathematical Description of Space and of Simple Media—Field Equations, Integral Forms of Field Equations, Electromagnetic Force, etc.; Transformation of Field and Force Equations; Electromagnetic Waves in Unbounded Regions; Skin Effect and Internal Impedance—in a solid cylindrical conductor, etc.; and Electrical Circuits—Analytical Foundations, Near-zone and quasi-near zone circuits, Balanced two-wire and four-wire transmission lines. Revised and enlarged version. New preface by the author. 5 appendices (Differential operators: Vector Formulas and Identities, etc.). Problems. Indexes. Bibliography. xvi + 580pp. 5⅜ x 8½.   S1023 Paperbound **$2.75**

Hydrodynamics

A TREATISE ON HYDRODYNAMICS, A. B. Basset. Favorite text on hydrodynamics for 2 genera-tions of physicists, hydrodynamical engineers, oceanographers, ship designers, etc. Clear enough for the beginning student, and thorough source for graduate students and engineers on the work of d'Alembert, Euler, Laplace, Lagrange, Poisson, Green, Clebsch, Stokes, Cauchy, Helmholtz, J. J. Thomson, Love, Hicks, Greenhill, Besant, Lamb, etc. Great amount of docu-mentation on entire theory of classical hydrodynamics. Vol I: theory of motion of frictionless liquids, vortex, and cyclic irrotational motion, etc. 132 exercises. Bibliography. 3 Appendices. xii + 264pp. Vol II: motion in viscous liquids, harmonic analysis, theory of tides, etc. 112 exercises, Bibliography. 4 Appendixes. xv + 328pp. Two volume set. 5⅜ x 8.
S724 Vol I Paperbound **$1.75**
S725 Vol II Paperbound **$1.75**
The set **$3.50**

HYDRODYNAMICS, Horace Lamb. Internationally famous complete coverage of standard refer-ence work on dynamics of liquids & gases. Fundamental theorems, equations, methods, solutions, background, for classical hydrodynamics. Chapters include Equations of Motion, Integration of Equations in Special Gases, Irrotational Motion, Motion of Liquid in 2 Dimen-sions, Motion of Solids through Liquid-Dynamical Theory, Vortex Motion, Tidal Waves, Surface Waves, Waves of Expansion, Viscosity, Rotating Masses of liquids. Excellently planned, ar-ranged; clear, lucid presentation. 6th enlarged, revised edition. Index. Over 900 footnotes, mostly bibliographical. 119 figures. xv + 738pp. 6⅛ x 9¼.   S256 Paperbound **$3.75**

HYDRODYNAMICS, H. Dryden, F. Murnaghan, Harry Bateman. Published by the National Research Council in 1932 this enormous volume offers a complete coverage of classical hydrodynamics. Encyclopedic in quality. Partial contents: physics of fluids, motion, turbulent flow, compressible fluids, motion in 1, 2, 3 dimensions; viscous fluids rotating, laminar motion, resistance of motion through viscous fluid, eddy viscosity, hydraulic flow in channels of various shapes, discharge of gases, flow past obstacles, etc. Bibliography of over 2,900 items. Indexes. 23 figures. 634pp. 5⅜ x 8.   S303 Paperbound **$2.75**

Mechanics, dynamics, thermodynamics, elasticity

MECHANICS, J. P. Den Hartog. Already a classic among introductory texts, the M.I.T. professor's lively and discursive presentation is equally valuable as a beginner's text, an engineering student's refresher, or a practicing engineer's reference. Emphasis in this highly readable text is on illuminating fundamental principles and showing how they are embodied in a great number of real engineering and design problems: trusses, loaded cables, beams, jacks, hoists, etc. Provides advanced material on relative motion and gyroscopes not usual in introductory texts. "Very thoroughly recommended to all those anxious to improve their real understanding of the principles of mechanics." MECHANICAL WORLD. Index. List of equations. 334 problems, all with answers. Over 550 diagrams and drawings. ix + 462pp. 5⅜ x 8.
S754 Paperbound **$2.00**

THEORETICAL MECHANICS: AN INTRODUCTION TO MATHEMATICAL PHYSICS, J. S. Ames, F. D. Murnaghan. A mathematically rigorous development of theoretical mechanics for the advanced student, with constant practical applications. Used in hundreds of advanced courses. An unusually thorough coverage of gyroscopic and baryscopic material, detailed analyses of the Coriolis acceleration, applications of Lagrange's equations, motion of the double pendulum, Hamilton-Jacobi partial differential equations, group velocity and dispersion, etc. Special relativity is also included. 159 problems. 44 figures. ix + 462pp. 5⅜ x 8.
S461 Paperbound **$2.25**

THEORETICAL MECHANICS: STATICS AND THE DYNAMICS OF A PARTICLE, W. D. MacMillan. Used for over 3 decades as a self-contained and extremely comprehensive advanced undergraduate text in mathematical physics, physics, astronomy, and deeper foundations of engineering. Early sections require only a knowledge of geometry; later, a working knowledge of calculus. Hundreds of basic problems, including projectiles to the moon, escape velocity, harmonic motion, ballistics, falling bodies, transmission of power, stress and strain, elasticity, astronomical problems. 340 practice problems plus many fully worked out examples make it possible to test and extend principles developed in the text. 200 figures. xvii + 430pp. 5⅜ x 8.   S467 Paperbound **$2.00**

THEORETICAL MECHANICS: THE THEORY OF THE POTENTIAL, W. D. MacMillan. A comprehensive, well balanced presentation of potential theory, serving both as an introduction and a reference work with regard to specific problems, for physicists and mathematicians. No prior knowledge of integral relations is assumed, and all mathematical material is developed as it becomes necessary. Includes: Attraction of Finite Bodies; Newtonian Potential Function; Vector Fields, Green and Gauss Theorems; Attractions of Surfaces and Lines; Surface Distribution of Matter; Two-Layer Surfaces; Spherical Harmonics; Ellipsoidal Harmonics; etc. "The great number of particular cases . . . should make the book valuable to geophysicists and others actively engaged in practical applications of the potential theory," Review of Scientific Instruments. Index. Bibliography. xiii + 469pp. 5⅜ x 8.   S486 Paperbound **$2.25**

THEORETICAL MECHANICS: DYNAMICS OF RIGID BODIES, W. D. MacMillan. Theory of dynamics of a rigid body is developed, using both the geometrical and analytical methods of instruction. Begins with exposition of algebra of vectors, it goes through momentum principles, motion in space, use of differential equations and infinite series to solve more sophisticated dynamics problems. Partial contents: moments of inertia, systems of free particles, motion parallel to a fixed plane, rolling motion, method of periodic solutions, much more. 82 figs. 199 problems. Bibliography. Indexes. xii + 476pp. 5⅜ x 8.   S641 Paperbound **$2.00**

MATHEMATICAL FOUNDATIONS OF STATISTICAL MECHANICS, A. I. Khinchin. Offering a precise and rigorous formulation of problems, this book supplies a thorough and up-to-date exposition. It provides analytical tools needed to replace cumbersome concepts, and furnishes for the first time a logical step-by-step introduction to the subject. Partial contents: geometry & kinematics of the phase space, ergodic problem, reduction to theory of probability, application of central limit problem, ideal monatomic gas, foundation of thermo-dynamics, dispersion and distribution of sum functions. Key to notations. Index. viii + 179pp. 5⅜ x 8.
S147 Paperbound **$1.50**

ELEMENTARY PRINCIPLES IN STATISTICAL MECHANICS, J. W. Gibbs. Last work of the great Yale mathematical physicist, still one of the most fundamental treatments available for advanced students and workers in the field. Covers the basic principle of conservation of probability of phase, theory of errors in the calculated phases of a system, the contributions of Clausius, Maxwell, Boltzmann, and Gibbs himself, and much more. Includes valuable comparison of statistical mechanics with thermodynamics: Carnot's cycle, mechanical definitions of entropy, etc. xvi + 208pp. 5⅜ x 8.   S707 Paperbound **$1.45**

PRINCIPLES OF MECHANICS AND DYNAMICS, Sir William Thomson (Lord Kelvin) and Peter Guthrie Tait. The principles and theories of fundamental branches of classical physics explained by two of the greatest physicists of all time. A broad survey of mechanics, with material on hydrodynamics, elasticity, potential theory, and what is now standard mechanics. Thorough and detailed coverage, with many examples, derivations, and topics not included in more recent studies. Only a knowledge of calculus is needed to work through this book. Vol. I (Preliminary): Kinematics; Dynamical Laws and Principles; Experience (observation, experimentation, formation of hypotheses, scientific method); Measures and Instruments; Continuous Calculating Machines. Vol. II (Abstract Dynamics): Statics of a Particle— Attraction; Statics of Solids and Fluids. Formerly Titled "Treatise on Natural Philosophy." Unabridged reprint of revised edition. Index. 168 diagrams. Total of xlii + 1035pp. 5⅜ x 8½.
Vol. I: S966 Paperbound **$2.35**
Vol. II: S967 Paperbound **$2.35**
Two volume Set Paperbound **$4.70**

INVESTIGATIONS ON THE THEORY OF THE BROWNIAN MOVEMENT, Albert Einstein. Reprints from rare European journals. 5 basic papers, including the Elementary Theory of the Brownian Movement, written at the request of Lorentz to provide a simple explanation. Translated by A. D. Cowper. Annotated, edited by R. Fürth. 33pp. of notes elucidate, give history of previous investigations. Author, subject indexes. 62 footnotes. 124pp. 5⅜ x 8.
S304 Paperbound **$1.25**

MECHANICS VIA THE CALCULUS, P. W. Norris, W. S. Legge. Covers almost everything, from linear motion to vector analysis: equations determining motion, linear methods, compounding of simple harmonic motions, Newton's laws of motion, Hooke's law, the simple pendulum, motion of a particle in 1 plane, centers of gravity, virtual work, friction, kinetic energy of rotating bodies, equilibrium of strings, hydrostatics, sheering stresses, elasticity, etc. 550 problems. 3rd revised edition. xii + 367pp. 6 x 9.
S207 Clothbound **$4.95**

THE DYNAMICS OF PARTICLES AND OF RIGID, ELASTIC, AND FLUID BODIES; BEING LECTURES ON MATHEMATICAL PHYSICS, A. G. Webster. The reissuing of this classic fills the need for a comprehensive work on dynamics. A wide range of topics is covered in unusually great depth, applying ordinary and partial differential equations. Part I considers laws of motion and methods applicable to systems of all sorts; oscillation, resonance, cyclic systems, etc. Part 2 is a detailed study of the dynamics of rigid bodies. Part 3 introduces the theory of potential; stress and strain, Newtonian potential functions, gyrostatics, wave and vortex motion, etc. Further contents: Kinematics of a point; Lagrange's equations; Hamilton's principle; Systems of vectors; Statics and dynamics of deformable bodies; much more, not easily found together in one volume. Unabridged reprinting of 2nd edition. 20 pages of notes on differential equations and the higher analysis. 203 illustrations. Selected bibliography. Index. xi + 588pp. 5⅜ x 8.
S522 Paperbound **$2.45**

A TREATISE ON DYNAMICS OF A PARTICLE, E. J. Routh. Elementary text on dynamics for beginning mathematics or physics student. Unusually detailed treatment from elementary definitions to motion in 3 dimensions, emphasizing concrete aspects. Much unique material important in recent applications. Covers impulsive forces, rectilinear and constrained motion in 2 dimensions, harmonic and parabolic motion, degrees of freedom, closed orbits, the conical pendulum, the principle of least action, Jacobi's method, and much more. Index. 559 problems, many fully worked out, incorporated into text. xiii + 418pp. 5⅜ x 8.
S696 Paperbound **$2.25**

DYNAMICS OF A SYSTEM OF RIGID BODIES (Elementary Section), E. J. Routh. Revised 7th edition of this standard reference. This volume covers the dynamical principles of the subject, and its more elementary applications: finding moments of inertia by integration, foci of inertia, d'Alembert's principle, impulsive forces, motion in 2 and 3 dimensions, Lagrange's equations, relative indicatrix, Euler's theorem, large tautochronous motions, etc. Index. 55 figures. Scores of problems. xv + 443pp. 5⅜ x 8.
S664 Paperbound **$2.50**

DYNAMICS OF A SYSTEM OF RIGID BODIES (Advanced Section), E. J. Routh. Revised 6th edition of a classic reference aid. Much of its material remains unique. Partial contents: moving axes, relative motion, oscillations about equilibrium, motion. Motion of a body under no forces, any forces. Nature of motion given by linear equations and conditions of stability. Free, forced vibrations, constants of integration, calculus of finite differences, variations, precession and nutation, motion of the moon, motion of string, chain, membranes. 64 figures. 498pp. 5⅜ x 8.
S229 Paperbound **$2.45**

DYNAMICAL THEORY OF GASES, James Jeans. Divided into mathematical and physical chapters for the convenience of those not expert in mathematics, this volume discusses the mathematical theory of gas in a steady state, thermodynamics, Boltzmann and Maxwell, kinetic theory, quantum theory, exponentials, etc. 4th enlarged edition, with new material on quantum theory, quantum dynamics, etc. Indexes. 28 figures. 444pp. 6⅛ x 9¼.
S136 Paperbound **$2.65**

THE THEORY OF HEAT RADIATION, Max Planck. A pioneering work in thermodynamics, providing basis for most later work, Nobel laureate Planck writes on Deductions from Electrodynamics and Thermodynamics, Entropy and Probability, Irreversible Radiation Processes, etc. Starts with simple experimental laws of optics, advances to problems of spectral distribution of energy and irreversibility. Bibliography. 7 illustrations. xiv + 224pp. 5⅜ x 8.
S546 Paperbound **$1.75**

FOUNDATIONS OF POTENTIAL THEORY, O. D. Kellogg. Based on courses given at Harvard this is suitable for both advanced and beginning mathematicians. Proofs are rigorous, and much material not generally available elsewhere is included. Partial contents: forces of gravity, fields of force, divergence theorem, properties of Newtonian potentials at points of free space, potentials as solutions of Laplace's equations, harmonic functions, electrostatics, electric images, logarithmic potential, etc. One of Grundlehren Series. ix + 384pp. 5⅜ x 8.
S144 Paperbound **$1.98**

THERMODYNAMICS, Enrico Fermi. Unabridged reproduction of 1937 edition. Elementary in treatment; remarkable for clarity, organization. Requires no knowledge of advanced math beyond calculus, only familiarity with fundamentals of thermometry, calorimetry. Partial Contents: Thermodynamic systems; First & Second laws of thermodynamics; Entropy; Thermodynamic potentials: phase rule, reversible electric cell; Gaseous reactions: van't Hoff reaction box, principle of LeChatelier; Thermodynamics of dilute solutions: osmotic & vapor pressures, boiling & freezing points; Entropy constant. Index. 25 problems. 24 illustrations. x + 160pp. 5⅜ x 8.
S361 Paperbound **$1.75**

THE THERMODYNAMICS OF ELECTRICAL PHENOMENA IN METALS and A CONDENSED COLLECTION OF THERMODYNAMIC FORMULAS, P. W. Bridgman. Major work by the Nobel Prizewinner: stimulating conceptual introduction to aspects of the electron theory of metals, giving an intuitive understanding of fundamental relationships concealed by the formal systems of Onsager and others. Elementary mathematical formulations show clearly the fundamental thermodynamical relationships of the electric field, and a complete phenomenological theory of metals is created. This is the work in which Bridgman announced his famous "thermomotive force" and his distinction between "driving" and "working" electromotive force. We have added in this Dover edition the author's long unavailable tables of thermodynamic formulas, extremely valuable for the speed of reference they allow. Two works bound as one. Index. 33 figures. Bibliography. xviii + 256pp. 5⅜ x 8. S723 Paperbound **$1.65**

TREATISE ON THERMODYNAMICS, Max Planck. Based on Planck's original papers this offers a uniform point of view for the entire field and has been used as an introduction for students who have studied elementary chemistry, physics, and calculus. Rejecting the earlier approaches of Helmholtz and Maxwell, the author makes no assumptions regarding the nature of heat, but begins with a few empirical facts, and from these deduces new physical and chemical laws. 3rd English edition of this standard text by a Nobel laureate. xvi + 297pp. 5⅜ x 8.
S219 Paperbound **$1.75**

THE MATHEMATICAL THEORY OF ELASTICITY, A. E. H. Love. A wealth of practical illustration combined with thorough discussion of fundamentals—theory, application, special problems and solutions. Partial Contents: Analysis of Strain & Stress, Elasticity of Solid Bodies, Elasticity of Crystals, Vibration of Spheres, Cylinders, Propagation of Waves in Elastic Solid Media, Torsion, Theory of Continuous Beams, Plates. Rigorous treatment of Volterra's theory of dislocations, 2-dimensional elastic systems, other topics of modern interest. "For years the standard treatise on elasticity," AMERICAN MATHEMATICAL MONTHLY. 4th revised edition. Index. 76 figures. xviii + 643pp. 6⅛ x 9¼.
S174 Paperbound **$3.00**

STRESS WAVES IN SOLIDS, H. Kolsky, Professor of Applied Physics, Brown University. The most readable survey of the theoretical core of current knowledge about the propagation of waves in solids, fully correlated with experimental research. Contents: Part I—Elastic Waves: propagation in an extended plastic medium, propagation in bounded elastic media, experimental investigations with elastic materials. Part II—Stress Waves in Imperfectly Elastic Media: internal friction, experimental investigations of dynamic elastic properties, plastic waves and shock waves, fractures produced by stress waves. List of symbols. Appendix. Supplemented bibliography. 3 full-page plates. 46 figures. x + 213pp. 5⅜ x 8½.
S1098 Paperbound **$1.55**

Relativity, quantum theory, atomic and nuclear physics

SPACE TIME MATTER, Hermann Weyl. "The standard treatise on the general theory of relativity" (Nature), written by a world-renowned scientist, provides a deep clear discussion of the logical coherence of the general theory, with introduction to all the mathematical tools needed: Maxwell, analytical geometry, non-Euclidean geometry, tensor calculus, etc. Basis is classical space-time, before absorption of relativity. Partial contents: Euclidean space, mathematical form, metrical continuum, relativity of time and space, general theory. 15 diagrams. Bibliography. New preface for this edition. xviii + 330pp. 5⅜ x 8.
S267 Paperbound **$2.00**

ATOMIC SPECTRA AND ATOMIC STRUCTURE, G. Herzberg. Excellent general survey for chemists, physicists specializing in other fields. Partial contents: simplest line spectra and elements of atomic theory, building-up principle and periodic system of elements, hyperfine structure of spectral lines, some experiments and applications. Bibliography. 80 figures. Index. xii + 257pp. 5⅜ x 8.
S115 Paperbound **$2.00**

PHYSICS, HISTORIES AND CLASSICS

A HISTORY OF PHYSICS: IN ITS ELEMENTARY BRANCHES (THROUGH 1925), INCLUDING THE EVOLUTION OF PHYSICAL LABORATORIES, Florian Cajori. Revised and enlarged edition. The only first-rate brief history of physics. Still the best entry for a student or teacher into the antecedents of modern theories of physics. A clear, non-mathematical, handy reference work which traces in critical fashion the developments of ideas, theories, techniques, and apparatus from the Greeks to the 1920's. Within each period he analyzes the basic topics of mechanics, light, electricity and magnetism, sound, atomic theory and structure of matter, radioactivity, etc. A chapter on modern research: Curie, Kelvin, Planck's quantum theory, thermodynamics, Fitzgerald and Lorentz, special and general relativity, J. J. Thomson's model of an atom, Bohr's discoveries and later results, wave mechanics, and many other matters. Much bibliographic detail in footnotes. Index. 16 figures. xv + 424pp. 5⅜ x 8. T970 Paperbound **$2.00**

A HISTORY OF THE MATHEMATICAL THEORIES OF ATTRACTION AND THE FIGURE OF THE EARTH: FROM THE TIME OF NEWTON TO THAT OF LAPLACE, I. Todhunter. A technical and detailed review of the theories concerning the shape of the earth and its gravitational pull, from the earliest investigations in the seventeenth century up to the middle of the nineteenth. Some of the greatest mathematicians and scientists in history applied themselves to these questions: Newton ("Principia Mathematica"), Huygens, Maupertuis, Simpson, d'Alembert, etc. Others discussed are Poisson, Gauss, Plana, Lagrange, Boit, and many more. Particular emphasis is placed on the theories of Laplace and Legendre, several chapters being devoted to Laplace's "Mécanique Céleste" and his memoirs, and several others to the memoirs of Legendre. Important to historians of science and mathematics and to the specialist who desires background information in the field. 2 volumes bound as 1. Index. xxxvi + 984pp. 5⅜ x 8.
S148 Clothbound **$7.50**

OPTICKS, Sir Isaac Newton. In its discussions of light, reflection, color, refraction, theories of wave and corpuscular theories of light, this work is packed with scores of insights and discoveries. In its precise and practical discussion of construction of optical apparatus, contemporary understandings of phenomena it is truly fascinating to modern physicists, astronomers, mathematicians. Foreword by Albert Einstein. Preface by I. B. Cohen of Harvard University. 7 pages of portraits, facsimile pages, letters, etc. cxvi + 414pp. 5⅜ x 8.
S205 Paperbound **$2.25**

TREATISE ON LIGHT, Christiaan Huygens. The famous original formulation of the wave theory of light, this readable book is one of the two decisive and definitive works in the field of light (Newton's "Optics" is the other). A scientific giant whose researches ranged over mathematics, astronomy, and physics, Huygens, in this historic work, covers such topics as rays propagated in straight lines, reflection and refraction, the spreading and velocity of light, the nature of opaque bodies, the non-spherical nature of light in the atmosphere, properties of Iceland Crystal, and other related matters. Unabridged republication of original (1912) English edition. Translated and introduced by Silvanus P. Thompson. 52 illustrations. xii + 129pp. 5⅜ x 8.
S179 Paperbound **$1.35**

FARADAY'S EXPERIMENTAL RESEARCHES IN ELECTRICITY. Faraday's historic series of papers containing the fruits of years of original experimentation in electrical theory and electrochemistry. Covers his findings in a variety of areas: Induction of electric currents, Evolution of electricity from magnetism, New electrical state or condition of matter, Explication of Arago's magnetic phenomena, New law of electric conduction, Electro-chemical decomposition, Electricity of the Voltaic Pile, Static Induction, Nature of the electric force or forces, Nature of electric current, The character and direction of the electric force of the Gymnotus, Magneto-electric spark, The magnetization of light and the illumination of magnetic lines of force, The possible relation of gravity to electricity, Sub-terraneous electro-telegraph wires, Some points of magnetic philosophy, The diamagnetic conditions of flame and gases, and many other matters. Complete and unabridged republication. 3 vols. bound as 2. Originally reprinted from the Philosophical Transactions of 1831-8. Indices. Illustrations. Total of 1463pp. 5⅜ x 8.
S783-4, Clothbound **$17.50** (tentative)

REFLECTIONS ON THE MOTIVE POWER OF FIRE, Sadi Carnot, and other papers on the 2nd law of thermodynamics by E. Clapeyron and R. Clausius. Carnot's "Reflections" laid the groundwork of modern thermodynamics. Its non-technical, mostly verbal statements examine the relations between heat and the work done by heat in engines, establishing conditions for the economical working of these engines. The papers by Clapeyron and Clausius here reprinted added further refinements to Carnot's work, and led to its final acceptance by physicists. Selections from posthumous manuscripts of Carnot are also included. All papers in English. New introduction by E. Mendoza. 12 illustrations. xxii + 152pp. 5⅜ x 8.
S661 Paperbound **$1.50**

DIALOGUES CONCERNING TWO NEW SCIENCES, Galileo Galilei. This classic of experimental science, mechanics, engineering, is as enjoyable as it is important. A great historical document giving insights into one of the world's most original thinkers, it is based on 30 years' experimentation. It offers a lively exposition of dynamics, elasticity, sound, ballistics, strength of materials, the scientific method. "Superior to everything else of mine," Galileo. Trans. by H. Crew, A. Salvio. 126 diagrams. Index. xxi + 288pp. 5⅜ x 8.
S99 Paperbound **$1.75**

TREATISE ON ELECTRICITY AND MAGNETISM, James Clerk Maxwell. For more than 80 years a seemingly inexhaustible source of leads for physicists, mathematicians, engineers. Total of 1082pp. on such topics as Measurement of Quantities, Electrostatics, Elementary Mathematical Theory of Electricity, Electrical Work and Energy in a System of Conductors, General Theorems, Theory of Electrical Images, Electrolysis, Conduction, Polarization, Dielectrics, Resistance, etc. "The greatest mathematical physicist since Newton," Sir James Jeans. 3rd edition. 107 figures, 21 plates. 1082pp. 5⅜ x 8.   S636-7, 2 volume set, paperbound **$4.00**

A HISTORY OF THE THEORY OF ELASTICITY AND THE STRENGTH OF MATERIALS, I. Todhunter and K. Pearson. For over 60 years a basic reference, unsurpassed in scope or authority. Both a history of the mathematical theory of elasticity from Galileo, Hooke, and Mariotte to Saint Venant, Kirchhoff, Clebsch, and Lord Kelvin and a detailed presentation of every important mathematical contribution during this period. Presents proofs of thousands of theorems and laws, summarizes every relevant treatise, many unavailable elsewhere. Practically a book apiece is devoted to modern founders: Saint Venant, Lamé, Boussinesq, Rankine, Lord Kelvin, F. Neumann, Kirchhoff, Clebsch. Hundreds of pages of technical and physical treatises on specific applications of elasticity to particular materials. Indispensable for the mathematician, physicist, or engineer working with elasticity. Unabridged, corrected reprint of original 3-volume 1886-1893 edition. Three volume set. Two indexes. Appendix to Vol. I. Total of 2344pp. 5⅜ x 8⅜.   S914–916 The set, Clothbound **$15.00**

DE MAGNETE, William Gilbert. This classic work on magnetism founded a new science. Gilbert was the first to use the word "electricity", to recognize mass as distinct from weight, to discover the effect of heat on magnetic bodies; invent an electroscope, differentiate between static electricity and magnetism, conceive of the earth as a magnet. Written by the first great experimental scientist, this lively work is valuable not only as an historical landmark, but as the delightfully easy to follow record of a perpetually searching, ingenious mind. Translated by P. F. Mottelay. 25-page biographical memoir. 90 figures. lix +368pp. 5⅜ x 8.   S470 Paperbound **$2.00**

ASTRONOMY

THE INTERNAL CONSTITUTION OF THE STARS, Sir A. S. Eddington. Influence of this has been enormous; first detailed exposition of theory of radiative equilibrium for stellar interiors, of all available evidence for existence of diffuse matter in interstellar space. Studies quantum theory, polytropic gas spheres, mass-luminosity relations, variable stars, etc. Discussions of equations paralleled with informal exposition of intimate relationship of astrophysics with great discoveries in atomic physics, radiation. Introduction. Appendix. Index. 421pp. 5⅜ x 8.   S563 Paperbound **$2.25**

PLANETARY THEORY, E. W. Brown and C. A. Shook. Provides a clear presentation of basic methods for calculating planetary orbits for today's astronomer. Begins with a careful exposition of specialized mathematical topics essential for handling perturbation theory and then goes on to indicate how most of the previous methods reduce ultimately to two general calculation methods: obtaining expressions either for the coordinates of planetary positions or for the elements which determine the perturbed paths. An example of each is given and worked in detail. Corrected edition. Preface. Appendix. Index. xii + 302pp. 5⅜ x 8½.   S1133 Paperbound **$2.25**

CANON OF ECLIPSES (CANON DER FINSTERNISSE), Prof. Theodor Ritter von Oppolzer. Since its original publication in 1887, this has been the standard reference and the most extensive single volume of data on the calculation of solar and lunar eclipses, past and future. A comprehensive introduction gives a full explanation of the use of the tables for the calculations of the exact dates of eclipses, etc. Data furnished for the calculation of 8,000 solar and 5,200 lunar eclipses, going back as far as 1200 B.C. and giving predictions up to the year 2161. Information is also given for partial and ring eclipses. All calculations based on Universal (Greenwich) Time. An unsurpassed reference work for astronomers, scientists engaged in space research and developments, historians, etc. Unabridged republication, with corrections. Preface to this edition by Donald Menzel and Owen Gingerich of the Harvard College Observatory. Translated by Owen Gingerich. 160 charts. lxx + 538pp. 8⅜ x 11¼.   S114 Clothbound **$10.00**

THEORY OF THE MOTION OF THE HEAVENLY BODIES MOVING ABOUT THE SUN IN CONIC SECTIONS, Karl Friedrich Gauss. A landmark of theoretical astronomy by the great German scientist. Still authoritative and invaluable to the practicing astronomer. Part I develops the relations between the quantities on which the motion about the sun of the heavenly bodies depends—relations pertaining simply to position in the orbit, simply to position in space, between several places in orbit, and between several places in space. The calculation methods of Part II based on the groundwork of Part I include: determination of an orbit from 3 complete observations, from 4 observations (of which only two are complete), determination of an orbit satisfying as nearly as possible any number of observations whatever, and determination of orbits, taking into account the perturbations. Translation of "Theoria Motus" and with an appendix by C. H. Davis. Unabridged republication. Appendices and tables. 13 figures. xviii + 376pp. 6½ x 9¼.   S1056 Paperbound **$2.95**

ENGINEERING AND TECHNOLOGY

General and mathematical

ENGINEERING MATHEMATICS, Kenneth S. Miller. A text for graduate students of engineering to strengthen their mathematical background in differential equations, etc. Mathematical steps very explicitly indicated. Contents: Determinants and Matrices, Integrals, Linear Differential Equations, Fourier Series and Integrals, Laplace Transform, Network Theory, Random Function . . . all vital requisites for advanced modern engineering studies. Unabridged republication. Appendices: Borel Sets; Riemann-Stieltjes Integral; Fourier Series and Integrals. Index. References at Chapter Ends. xii + 417pp. 6 x 8½.   S1121 Paperbound **$2.00**

MATHEMATICAL ENGINEERING ANALYSIS, Rufus Oldenburger. A book designed to assist the research engineer and scientist in making the transition from physical engineering situations to the corresponding mathematics. Scores of common practical situations found in all major fields of physics are supplied with their correct mathematical formulations—applications to automobile springs and shock absorbers, clocks, throttle torque of diesel engines, resistance networks, capacitors, transmission lines, microphones, neon tubes, gasoline engines, refrigeration cycles, etc. Each section reviews basic principles of underlying various fields: mechanics of rigid bodies, electricity and magnetism, heat, elasticity, fluid mechanics, and aerodynamics. Comprehensive and eminently useful. Index. 169 problems, answers. 200 photos and diagrams. xiv + 426pp. 5⅜ x 8½.   S919 Paperbound **$2.00**

MATHEMATICS OF MODERN ENGINEERING, E. G. Keller and R. E. Doherty. Written for the Advanced Course in Engineering of the General Electric Corporation, deals with the engineering use of determinants, tensors, the Heaviside operational calculus, dyadics, the calculus of variations, etc. Presents underlying principles fully, but purpose is to teach engineers to deal with modern engineering problems, and emphasis is on the perennial engineering attack of set-up and solve. Indexes. Over 185 figures and tables. Hundreds of exercises, problems, and worked-out examples. References. Two volume set. Total of xxxiii + 623pp. 5⅜ x 8.
S734 Vol I Paperbound **$1.85**
S735 Vol II Paperbound **$1.85**
The set **$3.70**

MATHEMATICAL METHODS FOR SCIENTISTS AND ENGINEERS, L. P. Smith. For scientists and engineers, as well as advanced math students. Full investigation of methods and practical description of conditions under which each should be used. Elements of real functions, differential and integral calculus, space geometry, theory of residues, vector and tensor analysis, series of Bessel functions, etc. Each method illustrated by completely-worked-out examples, mostly from scientific literature. 368 graded unsolved problems. 100 diagrams. x + 453pp. 5⅝ x 8⅜.   S220 Paperbound **$2.00**

THEORY OF FUNCTIONS AS APPLIED TO ENGINEERING PROBLEMS, edited by R. Rothe, F. Ollendorff, and K. Pohlhausen. A series of lectures given at the Berlin Institute of Technology that shows the specific applications of function theory in electrical and allied fields of engineering. Six lectures provide the elements of function theory in a simple and practical form, covering complex quantities and variables, integration in the complex plane, residue theorems, etc. Then 5 lectures show the exact uses of this powerful mathematical tool, with full discussions of problem methods. Index. Bibliography. 108 figures. x + 189pp. 5⅜ x 8.
S733 Paperbound **$1.35**

Aerodynamics and hydrodynamics

AIRPLANE STRUCTURAL ANALYSIS AND DESIGN, E. E. Sechler and L. G. Dunn. Systematic authoritative book which summarizes a large amount of theoretical and experimental work on structural analysis and design. Strong on classical subsonic material still basic to much aeronautic design . . . remains a highly useful source of information. Covers such areas as layout of the airplane, applied and design loads, stress-strain relationships for stable structures, truss and frame analysis, the problem of instability, the ultimate strength of stiffened flat sheet, analysis of cylindrical structures, wings and control surfaces, fuselage analysis, engine mounts, landing gears, etc. Originally published as part of the CALCIT Aeronautical Series. 256 Illustrations. 47 study problems. Indexes. xi + 420pp. 5⅜ x 8½.
S1043 Paperbound **$2.25**

FUNDAMENTALS OF HYDRO- AND AEROMECHANICS, L. Prandtl and O. G. Tietjens. The well-known standard work based upon Prandtl's lectures at Goettingen. Wherever possible hydrodynamics theory is referred to practical considerations in hydraulics, with the view of unifying theory and experience. Presentation is extremely clear and though primarily physical, mathematical proofs are rigorous and use vector analysis to a considerable extent. An Enginering Society Monograph, 1934. 186 figures. Index. xvi + 270pp. 5⅜ x 8.
S374 Paperbound **$1.85**

Catalogue of Dover Books

FLUID MECHANICS FOR HYDRAULIC ENGINEERS, H. Rouse. Standard work that gives a coherent picture of fluid mechanics from the point of view of the hydraulic engineer. Based on courses given to civil and mechanical engineering students at Columbia and the California Institute of Technology, this work covers every basic principle, method, equation, or theory of interest to the hydraulic engineer. Much of the material, diagrams, charts, etc., in this self-contained text are not duplicated elsewhere. Covers irrotational motion, conformal mapping, problems in laminar motion, fluid turbulence, flow around immersed bodies, transportation of sediment, general charcteristics of wave phenomena, gravity waves in open channels, etc. Index. Appendix of physical properties of common fluids. Frontispiece + 245 figures and photographs. xvi + 422pp. 5⅜ x 8.
S729 Paperbound **$2.25**

WATERHAMMER ANALYSIS, John Parmakian. Valuable exposition of the graphical method of solving waterhammer problems by Assistant Chief Designing Engineer, U.S. Bureau of Reclamation. Discussions of rigid and elastic water column theory, velocity of waterhammer waves, theory of graphical waterhammer analysis for gate operation, closings, openings, rapid and slow movements, etc., waterhammer in pump discharge caused by power failure, waterhammer analysis for compound pipes, and numerous related problems. "With a concise and lucid style, clear printing, adequate bibliography and graphs for approximate solutions at the project stage, it fills a vacant place in waterhammer literature," WATER POWER. 43 problems. Bibliography. Index. 113 illustrations. xiv + 161pp. 5⅜ x 8½.
S1061 Paperbound **$1.65**

AERODYNAMIC THEORY: A GENERAL REVIEW OF PROGRESS, William F. Durand, editor-in-chief. A monumental joint effort by the world's leading authorities prepared under a grant of the Guggenheim Fund for the Promotion of Aeronautics. Intended to provide the student and aeronautic designer with the theoretical and experimental background of aeronautics. Never equalled for breadth, depth, reliability. Contains discussions of special mathematical topics not usually taught in the engineering or technical courses. Also: an extended two-part treatise on Fluid Mechanics, discussions of aerodynamics of perfect fluids, analyses of experiments with wind tunnels, applied airfoil theory, the non-lifting system of the airplane, the air propeller, hydrodynamics of boats and floats, the aerodynamics of cooling, etc. Contributing experts include Munk, Giacomelli, Prandtl, Toussaint, Von Karman, Klemperer, among others. Unabridged republication. 6 volumes bound as 3. Total of 1,012 figures, 12 plates. Total of 2,186pp. Bibliographies. Notes. Indices. 5⅜ x 8.
S328-S330 Clothbound, The Set **$17.50**

APPLIED HYDRO- AND AEROMECHANICS, L. Prandtl and O. G. Tietjens. Presents, for the most part, methods which will be valuable to engineers. Covers flow in pipes, boundary layers, airfoil theory, entry conditions, turbulent flow in pipes, and the boundary layer, determining drag from measurements of pressure and velocity, etc. "Will be welcomed by all students of aerodynamics," NATURE. Unabridged, unaltered. An Engineering Society Monograph, 1934. Index. 226 figures, 28 photographic plates illustrating flow patterns. xvi + 311pp. 5⅜ x 8.
S375 Paperbound **$1.85**

SUPERSONIC AERODYNAMICS, E. R. C. Miles. Valuable theoretical introduction to the supersonic domain, with emphasis on mathematical tools and principles, for practicing aerodynamicists and advanced students in aeronautical engineering. Covers fundamental theory, divergence theorem and principles of circulation, compressible flow and Helmholtz laws, the Prandtl-Busemann graphic method for 2-dimensional flow, oblique shock waves, the Taylor-Maccoll method for cones in supersonic flow, the Chaplygin method for 2-dimensional flow, etc. Problems range from practical engineering problems to development of theoretical results. "Rendered outstanding by the unprecedented scope of its contents . . . has undoubtedly filled a vital gap," AERONAUTICAL ENGINEERING REVIEW. Index. 173 problems, answers. 106 diagrams. 7 tables. xii + 255pp. 5⅜ x 8.
S214 Paperbound **$1.45**

HYDRAULIC TRANSIENTS, G. R. Rich. The best text in hydraulics ever printed in English . . . by one of America's foremost engineers (former Chief Design Engineer for T.V.A.). Provides a transition from the basic differential equations of hydraulic transient theory to the arithmetic intergration computation required by practicing engineers. Sections cover Water Hammer, Turbine Speed Regulation, Stability of Governing, Water-Hammer Pressures in Pump Discharge Lines, The Differential and Restricted Orifice Surge Tanks, The Normalized Surge Tank Charts of Calame and Gaden, Navigation Locks, Surges in Power Canals—Tidal Harmonics, etc. Revised and enlarged. Author's prefaces. Index. xiv + 409pp. 5⅜ x 8½.
S116 Paperbound **$2.50**

HYDRAULICS AND ITS APPLICATIONS, A. H. Gibson. Excellent comprehensive textbook for the student and thorough practical manual for the professional worker, a work of great stature in its area. Half the book is devoted to theory and half to applications and practical problems met in the field. Covers modes of motion of a fluid, critical velocity, viscous flow, eddy formation, Bernoulli's theorem, flow in converging passages, vortex motion, form of effluent streams, notches and weirs, skin friction, losses at valves and elbows, siphons, erosion of channels, jet propulsion, waves of oscillation, and over 100 similar topics. Final chapters (nearly 400 pages) cover more than 100 kinds of hydraulic machinery: Pelton wheel, speed regulators, the hydraulic ram, surge tanks, the scoop wheel, the Venturi meter, etc. A special chapter treats methods of testing theoretical hypotheses: scale models of rivers, tidal estuaries, siphon spillways, etc. 5th revised and enlarged (1952) edition. Index. Appendix. 427 photographs and diagrams. 95 examples, answers. xv + 813pp. 6 x 9.
S791 Clothbound **$8.00**

Catalogue of Dover Books

FLUID MECHANICS THROUGH WORKED EXAMPLES, D. R. L. Smith and J. Houghton. Advanced text covering principles and applications to practical situations. Each chapter begins with concise summaries of fundamental ideas. 163 fully worked out examples applying principles outlined in the text. 275 other problems, with answers. Contents: The Pressure of Liquids on Surfaces; Floating Bodies; Flow Under Constant Head in Pipes; Circulation; Vorticity; The Potential Function; Laminar Flow and Lubrication; Impact of Jets; Hydraulic Turbines; Centrifugal and Reciprocating Pumps; Compressible Fluids; and many other items. Total of 438 examples. 250 line illustrations. 340pp. Index. 6 x 8⅞.   S981 Clothbound **$6.00**

THEORY OF SHIP MOTIONS, S. N. Blagoveshchensky. The only detailed text in English in a rapidly developing branch of engineering and physics, it is the work of one of the world's foremost authorities—Blagoveshchensky of Leningrad Shipbuilding Institute. A senior-level treatment written primarily for engineering students, but also of great importance to naval architects, designers, contractors, researchers in hydrodynamics, and other students. No mathematics beyond ordinary differential equations is required for understanding the text. Translated by T. & L. Strelkoff, under editorship of Louis Landweber, Iowa Institute of Hydraulic Research, under auspices of Office of Naval Research. Bibliography. Index. 231 diagrams and illustrations. Total of 649pp. 5⅜ x 8½.   Vol. I: S234 Paperbound **$2.00**
Vol. II: S235 Paperbound **$2.00**

THEORY OF FLIGHT, Richard von Mises. Remains almost unsurpassed as balanced, well-written account of fundamental fluid dynamics, and situations in which air compressibility effects are unimportant. Stressing equally theory and practice, avoiding formidable mathematical structure, it conveys a full understanding of physical phenomena and mathematical concepts. Contains perhaps the best introduction to general theory of stability. "Outstanding," Scientific, Medical, and Technical Books. New introduction by K. H. Hohenemser. Bibliographical, historical notes. Index. 408 illustrations. xvi + 620pp. 5⅜ x 8⅜.   S541 Paperbound **$2.95**

THEORY OF WING SECTIONS, I. H. Abbott, A. E. von Doenhoff. Concise compilation of subsonic aerodynamic characteristics of modern NASA wing sections, with description of their geometry, associated theory. Primarily reference work for engineers, students, it gives methods, data for using wing-section data to predict characteristics. Particularly valuable: chapters on thin wings, airfoils; complete summary of NACA's experimental observations, system of construction families of airfoils. 350pp. of tables on Basic Thickness Forms, Mean Lines, Airfoil Ordinates, Aerodynamic Characteristics of Wing Sections. Index. Bibliography. 191 illustrations. Appendix. 705pp. 5⅜ x 8.   S558 Paperbound **$3.25**

WEIGHT-STRENGTH ANALYSIS OF AIRCRAFT STRUCTURES, F. R. Shanley. Scientifically sound methods of analyzing and predicting the structural weight of aircraft and missiles. Deals directly with forces and the distances over which they must be transmitted, making it possible to develop methods by which the minimum structural weight can be determined for any material and conditions of loading. Weight equations for wing and fuselage structures. Includes author's original papers on inelastic buckling and creep buckling. "Particularly successful in presenting his analytical methods for investigating various optimum design principles," AERONAUTICAL ENGINEERING REVIEW. Enlarged bibliography. Index. 199 figures. xiv + 404pp. 5⅝ x 8⅜.   S660 Paperbound **$2.50**

Electricity

TWO-DIMENSIONAL FIELDS IN ELECTRICAL ENGINEERING, L. V. Bewley. A useful selection of typical engineering problems of interest to practicing electrical engineers. Introduces senior students to the methods and procedures of mathematical physics. Discusses theory of functions of a complex variable, two-dimensional fields of flow, general theorems of mathematical physics and their applications, conformal mapping or transformation, method of images, freehand flux plotting, etc. New preface by the author. Appendix by W. F. Kiltner. Index. Bibliography at chapter ends. xiv + 204pp. 5⅜ x 8½.   S1118 Paperbound **$1.50**

FLUX LINKAGES AND ELECTROMAGNETIC INDUCTION, L. V. Bewley. A brief, clear book which shows proper uses and corrects misconceptions of Faraday's law of electromagnetic induction in specific problems. Contents: Circuits, Turns, and Flux Linkages; Substitution of Circuits; Electromagnetic Induction; General Criteria for Electromagnetic Induction; Applications and Paradoxes; Theorem of Constant Flux Linkages. New Section: Rectangular Coil in a Varying Uniform Medium. Valuable supplement to class texts for engineering students. Corrected, enlarged edition. New preface. Bibliography in notes. 49 figures. xi + 106pp. 5⅜ x 8.   S1103 Paperbound **$1.25**

INDUCTANCE CALCULATIONS: WORKING FORMULAS AND TABLES, Frederick W. Grover. An invaluable book to everyone in electrical engineering. Provides simple single formulas to cover all the more important cases of inductance. The approach involves only those parameters that naturally enter into each situation, while extensive tables are given to permit easy interpolations. Will save the engineer and student countless hours and enable them to obtain accurate answers with minimal effort. Corrected republication of 1946 edition. 58 tables. 97 completely worked out examples. 66 figures. xiv + 286pp. 5⅜ x 8½.   S974 Paperbound **$1.85**

GEOLOGY, GEOGRAPHY, METEOROLOGY

PRINCIPLES OF STRATIGRAPHY, A. W. Grabau. Classic of 20th century geology, unmatched in scope and comprehensiveness. Nearly 600 pages cover the structure and origins of every kind of sedimentary, hydrogenic, oceanic, pyroclastic, atmoclastic, hydroclastic, marine hydroclastic, and bioclastic rock; metamorphism; erosion; etc. Includes also the constitution of the atmosphere; morphology of oceans, rivers, glaciers; volcanic activities; faults and earthquakes; and fundamental principles of paleontology (nearly 200 pages). New introduction by Prof. M. Kay, Columbia U. 1277 bibliographical entries. 264 diagrams. Tables, maps, etc. Two volume set. Total of xxxii + 1185pp. 5⅜ x 8.
S686 Vol I Paperbound **$2.50**
S687 Vol II Paperbound **$2.50**
The set **$5.00**

TREATISE ON SEDIMENTATION, William H. Twenhofel. A milestone in the history of geology, this two-volume work, prepared under the auspices of the United States Research Council, contains practically everything known about sedimentation up to 1932. Brings together all the findings of leading American and foreign geologists and geographers and has never been surpassed for completeness, thoroughness of description, or accuracy of detail. Vol. 1 discusses the sources and production of sediments, their transportation, deposition, diagenesis, and lithification. Also modification of sediments by organisms and topographical, climatic, etc. conditions which contribute to the alteration of sedimentary processes. 220 pages deal with products of sedimentation: minerals, limestones, dolomites, coals, etc. Vol. 2 continues the examination of products such as gypsum and saline residues, silica, strontium, manganese, etc. An extensive exposition of structures, textures and colors of sediments: stratification, cross-lamination, ripple mark, oolitic and pisolitic textures, etc. Chapters on environments or realms of sedimentation and field and laboratory techniques are also included. Indispensable to modern-day geologists and students. Index. List of authors cited. 1733-item bibliography. 121 diagrams. Total of xxxiii + 926pp. 5⅜ x 8½.
Vol. I: S950 Paperbound **$2.50**
Vol. II: S951 Paperbound **$2.50**
Two volume set Paperbound **$5.00**

THE EVOLUTION OF THE IGNEOUS ROCKS, N. L. Bowen. Invaluable serious introduction applies techniques of physics and chemistry to explain igneous rock diversity in terms of chemical composition and fractional crystallization. Discusses liquid immiscibility in silicate magmas, crystal sorting, liquid lines of descent, fractional resorption of complex minerals, petrogenesis, etc. Of prime importance to geologists & mining engineers, also to physicists, chemists working with high temperatures and pressures. "Most important," TIMES, London. 3 indexes. 263 bibliographic notes. 82 figures. xviii + 334pp. 5⅜ x 8.
S311 Paperbound **$2.00**

INTERNAL CONSTITUTION OF THE EARTH, edited by Beno Gutenberg. Completely revised. Brought up-to-date, reset. Prepared for the National Research Council this is a complete & thorough coverage of such topics as earth origins, continent formation, nature & behavior of the earth's core, petrology of the crust, cooling forces in the core, seismic & earthquake material, gravity, elastic constants, strain characteristics and similar topics. "One is filled with admiration . . . a high standard . . . there is no reader who will not learn something from this book," London, Edinburgh, Dublin, Philosophic Magazine. Largest bibliography in print: 1127 classified items. Indexes. Tables of constants. 43 diagrams. 439pp. 6⅛ x 9¼.
S414 Paperbound **$3.00**

HYDROLOGY, edited by Oscar E. Meinzer. Prepared for the National Research Council. Detailed complete reference library on precipitation, evaporation, snow, snow surveying, glaciers, lakes, infiltration, soil moisture, ground water, runoff, drought, physical changes produced by water, hydrology of limestone terranes, etc. Practical in application, especially valuable for engineers. 24 experts have created "the most up-to-date, most complete treatment of the subject," AM. ASSOC. of PETROLEUM GEOLOGISTS. Bibliography. Index. 165 illustrations. xi + 712pp. 6⅛ x 9¼.
S191 Paperbound **$3.25**

SNOW CRYSTALS, W. A. Bentley and W. J. Humphreys. Over 200 pages of Bentley's famous microphotographs of snow flakes—the product of painstaking, methodical work at his Jericho, Vermont studio. The pictures, which also include plates of frost, glaze and dew on vegetation, spider webs, windowpanes; sleet; graupel or soft hail, were chosen both for their scientific interest and their aesthetic qualities. The wonder of nature's diversity is exhibited in the intricate, beautiful patterns of the snow flakes. Introductory text by W. J. Humphreys. Selected bibliography. 2,453 illustrations. 224pp. 8 x 10¼.
T287 Paperbound **$2.95**

PHYSICS OF THE AIR, W. J. Humphreys. A very thorough coverage of classical materials and theories in meteorology . . . written by one of this century's most highly respected physical meteorologists. Contains the standard account in English of atmospheric optics. 5 main sections: Mechanics and Thermodynamics of the Atmosphere, Atmospheric Electricity and Auroras, Meteorological Acoustics, Atmospheric Optics, and Factors of Climatic Control. Under these headings, topics covered are: theoretical relations between temperature, pressure, and volume in the atmosphere; composition, pressure, and density; circulation; evaporation and condensation; fog, clouds, thunderstorms, lightning; aurora polaris; principal ice-age theories; etc. New preface by Prof. Julius London. 226 illustrations. Index. xviii + 676pp. 5⅜ x 8½.
S1044 Paperbound **$3.00**

Catalogue of Dover Books

URANIUM PROSPECTING, H. L. Barnes. For immediate practical use, professional geologist considers uranium ores, geological occurrences, field conditions, all aspects of highly profitable occupation. Index. Bibliography. x + 117pp. 5⅜ x 8. **T309 Paperbound $1.00**

SELECTED PAPERS IN THE THEORY OF THERMAL CONVECTION: WITH SPECIAL APPLICATION TO THE EARTH'S PLANETARY ATMOSPHERE, Edited by Barry Saltzman. An indispensable volume for anyone interested in the motions of the earth's atmosphere. 25 basic theoretical papers on thermal convection by major scientists, past and present: Helmholtz, Overbeck, Jeffreys, Rayleigh, G. I. Taylor, Chandrasekhar, A. R. Low, Rossby, Davies, Charney, Eady, Phillips, Pellew and Southwell, Elbert, Fjortoft, and H.-L. Kuo. Bibliography. x + 461pp. 6⅛ x 9¼. **S171 Paperbound $3.00**

THE FOUNDERS OF GEOLOGY, Sir Archibald Geikie. Survey of the high moments and the work of the major figures of the period in which the main foundations of modern geology were laid—the latter half of the 18th century to the first half of the 19th. The developments in the science during this era centering around the lives and accomplishments of the great contributors: Palissy, Guettard, Demarest, Pallas, Lehmann, Füchsel, Werner, Hutton, Playfair, Sir James Hall, Cuvier, Lyell, Logan, Darwin, Agassiz, Nicol, and others. Comprehensive and readable. Index. xi + 486pp. 5⅜ x 8½. **T352 Paperbound $2.25**

THE BIRTH AND DEVELOPMENT OF THE GEOLOGICAL SCIENCES, F. D. Adams. Most thorough history of the earth sciences ever written. Geological thought from earliest times to the end of the 19th century, covering over 300 early thinkers & systems: fossils & their explanation, vulcanists vs. neptunists, figured stones & paleontology, generation of stones, dozens of similar topics. 91 illustrations, including medieval, renaissance woodcuts, etc. Index. 632 footnotes, mostly bibliographical. 511pp. 5⅜ x 8. **T5 Paperbound $2.25**

A HISTORY OF ANCIENT GEOGRAPHY, E. H. Bunbury. Standard study, in English, of ancient geography; never equalled for scope, detail. First full account of history of geography from Greeks' first world picture based on mariners, through Ptolemy. Discusses every important map, discovery, figure, travel, expedition, war, conjecture, narrative, bearing on subject. Chapters on Homeric geography, Herodotus, Alexander expedition, Strabo, Pliny, Ptolemy, would stand alone as exhaustive monographs. Includes minor geographers, men not usually regarded in this context: Hecataeus, Pythea, Hipparchus, Artemidorus, Marinus of Tyre, etc. Uses information gleaned from military campaigns such as Punic wars, Hannibal's passage of Alps, campaigns of Lucullus, Pompey, Caesar's wars, the Trojan war. New introduction by W. H. Stahl, Brooklyn College. Bibliography. Index. 20 maps. 1426pp. 5⅜ x 8. **T570-1, clothbound, 2 volume set $12.50**

DE RE METALLICA, Georgius Agricola. 400-year old classic translated, annotated by former President Herbert Hoover. The first scientific study of mineralogy and mining, for over 200 years after its appearance in 1556, it was the standard treatise. 12 books, exhaustively annotated, discuss the history of mining, selection of sites, types of deposits, making pits, shafts, ventilating, pumps, crushing machinery; assaying, smelting, refining metals; also salt, alum, nitre, glass making. Definitive edition, with all 289 16th century woodcuts of the original. Biographical, historical introductions, bibliography, survey of ancient authors. Indexes. A fascinating book for anyone interested in art, history of science, geology, etc. Deluxe edition. 289 illustrations. 672pp. 6¾ x 10¾. Library cloth. **S6 Clothbound $10.00**

GEOGRAPHICAL ESSAYS, William Morris Davis. Modern geography & geomorphology rest on the fundamental work of this scientist. 26 famous essays presenting most important theories, field researches. Partial contents: Geographical Cycle, Plains of Marine and Subaerial Denudation, The Peneplain, Rivers and Valleys of Pennsylvania, Outline of Cape Cod, Sculpture of Mountains by Glaciers, etc. "Long the leader & guide," ECONOMIC GEOGRAPHY. "Part of the very texture of geography . . . models of clear thought," GEOGRAPHIC REVIEW. Index. 130 figures. vi + 777pp. 5⅜ x 8. **S383 Paperbound $2.95**

Prices subject to change without notice.

Dover publishes books on art, music, philosophy, literature, languages, history, social sciences, psychology, handcrafts, orientalia, puzzles and entertainments, chess, pets and gardens, books explaining science, intermediate and higher mathematics, mathematical physics, engineering, biological sciences, earth sciences, classics of science, etc. Write to:

Dept. catrr.
Dover Publications, Inc.
180 Varick Street, N.Y. 14, N.Y.